An Introduction to Qigong

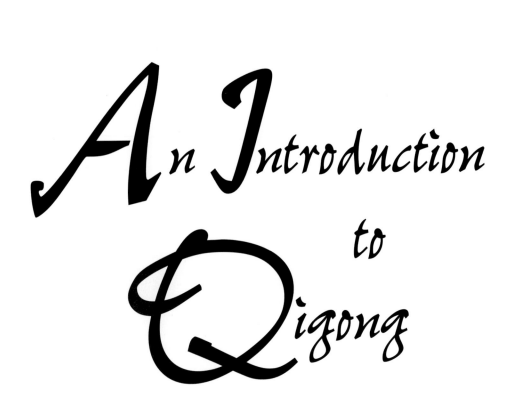

An Introduction to Qigong

RAY PAWLETT

Published by SILVERDALE BOOKS
An imprint of Bookmart Ltd
Registered number 2372865
Trading as Bookmart Ltd
Desford Road
Enderby
Leicester LE9 5AD

© 2002 D&S Books

D&S Books
Cottage Meadow, Bocombe,
Parkham, Bideford
Devon, England
EX39 5PH

e-mail us at:-
enquiries.dspublishing@care4free.net

This edition printed 2002

ISBN 1-856056-33-3

Creative Director: *Sarah King*
Editor: *Yvonne Worth*
Project editor: *Anna Southgate*
Photographer: *Colin Bowling*
Designer: *Dave Jones*

Printed in China

1 3 5 7 9 10 8 6 4 2

$\mathcal{C}$ontents

Introduction

What is music? What is science? These questions are quite difficult to answer, because the subjects of music and science are so broad-reaching that it is impossible to define them in simple terms. In a way, the question is meaningless if it cannot have an answer, yet we all know what music and science are because they are part of our culture.

Qigong can be thought of in similar terms. Its scope is so wide that it defies a "What is Qigong?" question. Yet, to many Eastern cultures, and those trained in the subject, a personal definition is easy.

One of the aims of here is to present some of the facts and introduce a selection of exercises that will allow the reader to form his or her own definition of Qigong. There are literally thousands of different styles of Qigong. This book attempts to condense a small selection from some of the most common methods into a format that can be easily understood and absorbed.

The book begins by presenting some basic information about Qigong before attempting to describe the exercises themselves. For the reader who is eager to start with the actual business of doing the exercises, I would recommend that the chapter "Is it For Me and What do I Need?" should be digested. It is also essential to warm up before attempting the exercises.

This book can help you to learn some of the basic Qigong movements and theory but is not designed to replace a teacher. It should never be used to replace a doctor or therapist. Should you be in any doubt as to the suitability of the exercises, consult your doctor before attempting the exercise.

What is Qigong?

If you develop an interest in the Eastern martial arts and healing arts, it will not be long before you read about Qigong experts who claim to be well over one hundred years old and still teaching the art, or before you discover the seemingly impossible feats of martial artists such as the Shaolin monks. As you delve deeper, you will find others who claim telepathic abilities or even the ability to fight aggressors from a distance without even touching them.

The common training method for them all will be some kind of Qigong practice. In my opinion, many of the wilder claims are best considered as folk legends. Some of these "superhuman" skills however have been witnessed by thousands. Many have watched in awe as the Shaolin monks demonstrate their ability to withstand blows and attacks that could kill a person without similar years of training.

A literal translation of Qigong is "energy combined with skill". Obviously this is a broad definition. On consideration you may be able to think of a variety of different cultures that practice the system of Qigong but do not give it the same name. Examples of this are yoga, martial arts, some Shamanic exercises and even Reichian therapy.

The areas of Qigong that this book examines all stem from the Chinese and Japanese cultures. If you have studied any other energy methods, you may also find similarities. A good reason for this is the antiquity of Qigong methods. There is archaeological evidence of Qigong dating back to 600 BC, i.e. the "Jade Pendant Inscription on Qigong". Since that time various masters have developed their work but with a different emphasis, depending on their physical and energetic makeup. Obviously, in nearly two and a half thousand years, there will be many overlaps.

Another reason will simply be that there is a logical limit to what a human being can do with two arms and two legs!

Is It For Me and What Do I Need?

Qigong is practised all around the world by millions of people of all shapes, sizes, fitness levels and age. If you want to learn Qigong, there is certain to be a style or a teacher somewhere who can guide you.

One of the advantages of Qigong over some of the other styles of energy-building exercises is that you need very little room to practise. Therefore, even if your lifestyle demands that you travel and stay in hotels, you can still practise effectively. Many businessmen find Qigong a particularly useful form of exercise, as it is also very good for stress and posture problems that may come from sitting at a desk or in a car for long periods.

Many women have found that Qigong can help them during and after pregnancy. People with serious health problems have also found comfort in Qigong. Remember, you will always have better results if you can find a good teacher.

Unlike some martial arts' disciplines, there is no uniform for Qigong. Simply find yourself some loose-fitting clothes and some comfortable shoes. There is nothing to stop you training barefoot as long as your feet do not get cold!

A word of warning concerning teachers. Some teachers will employ very powerful and disorientating techniques in their lessons. This can leave the student vulnerable to the teacher or to other group members. A common trick is for them to openly criticise your parents, accusing them of injustices against you. If you ever find yourself in this type of situation, my advice is to get out immediately. You have probably stumbled upon a cult that employs energetic methods in a similar way to the brainwashing experiments of the mid-seventies.

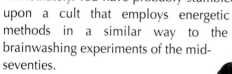

Listen to Yourself

Qigong exercises are generally designed to be comfortable for your body. Unlike many gymnasium-taught exercises, you should not need to "grit your teeth" to get through your set of exercises.

Instead, Qigong works in a much less forced way. You will gradually increase your energy and strength through regular and consistent practice. The idea of having two or three hard workouts in a week is incompatible with the more natural flow of learning Qigong.

This makes some of the exercises appear deceptively easy. It is common to join a class and see somebody who you think is less fit than yourself practising exercises that are quite difficult. If you try to copy them, rather than listening for your own inner voice to tell you when you need to stop, you will risk injury.

Qigong exercises and pain do not go together. If any of the exercises hurt, whether it is a stretch or even sitting in one position for meditation for any length of time, you should stop the exercise. It means that you need to do some work before that exercise is suitable for you. Do not think that this is any judgement on you or your abilities, the next exercise could well be one that you find easy and your classmate finds difficult.

The rule for the exercises is to take them slowly, so that you recognise when you enter your "danger zone". If you start to experience pain or discomfort, come out of the exercise slowly, being careful not to damage yourself.

Remember, also, that Qigong works with the emotional body as well as the physical body. If you find that a Qigong practice session causes some kind of emotional release, do not be too alarmed. Give yourself time to work it through at it's own pace and always follow the advice of your teacher. It is normally simply an example of your body and emotions trying to find a more balanced state after becoming activated by the Qigong exercises.

The Emperor's New Clothes

Most people know the children's story about the "Emperor's new clothes". As with many traditional fairytales, there is a useful lesson to be learned from it. From teaching Tai Chi and Qigong for many years, it seems, unfortunately, to be a lesson that is easily forgotten!

The story goes that a powerful Emperor wanted the most fashionable new outfit in the land. He called the master tailors to show their wares, but none could win the Emperor's favour.

Finally, a clever merchant convinced the Emperor that he had the best suit in the land and that only a fool would question its quality. When the Emperor "tried on" the suit, there was actually no suit at all – the Emperor was completely naked. However, reluctant to appear a fool, the Emperor bought the "suit" for a high price.

Not wishing to offend the Emperor or question his expensive investment, the courtiers were afraid to tell him that he had been duped. That is, until a young boy exclaimed that the Emperor had no clothes, and the spell was broken.

This story can be relived in some Qigong classes. Some teachers will explain different "energies" in such a way that students feel they must be stupid or insensitive if they are unable to sense the energy for themselves. Rather than questioning the teacher, the students sometimes convince themselves that they are actually having the same experience.

It is true that you need to follow a teacher's guidance when learning any subject, but it is important to balance that need with your own intelligence. Is the teacher being genuine or is he following his own agenda? Are you being true to yourself? If you can answer both of these questions, there is a good chance that you will not be like the Emperor.

Balancing Opposites

The story of the Emperor's new clothes introduces a concept that is vital to all holistic healing therapies – balance. To a martial artist, balance is vital in order to be able to transmit power. The healer will use his techniques to balance the energies and emotions within the body. In Western terms, the toils of the scientist are fruitless unless theory can be balanced with application outside the laboratory (even though the theory may take many generations to get out of the laboratory).

So why is balance important? A crucial aspect of balance is that if you are balanced, it is easier for you to stay "centred" or "grounded". If you are both centred and grounded, then you will be able to go about your daily routine in a more relaxed and efficient way and therefore waste less of your vital energy. The result of this is that you allow your body a better chance of avoiding external attacks or of recovering better if they do occur.

Qigong can reduce the stressful effect of being in a busy city.

A visit to a busy city will give you an illustration of this. If you watch the crowd in a busy area for a few moments, you will notice patterns in the movements. You will see the type of person who is always rushing. Normally their chin will be pushed forwards and their shoulders hunched. As they make their way across the street, their path will be erratic as they try to avoid bumping into other people who are also in a rush. This will cause them to use much more energy than if they had taken the time to observe who or what they might collide into. Normally, by the time they get home, they will be exhausted.

The problem here is that this person has most of their attention in the future instead of in the present moment. By rushing from one thing to the next, he is not allowing himself to feel the present situation and it becomes impossible to "go with the flow". Balancing makes it easier to live in the moment, rather than allowing the future to take control.

Energy

When you enter a room and switch on the light, the only thing that normally concerns you is that the room is light enough for you to see. The fact that some invisible form of energy has travelled through a wiring system to a unit that can transform electrical energy into light energy is of little concern to those who are not scientists or engineers.

According to the world view of many cultures, and to an increasing quantity of scientific researchers, our bodies have an energy that operates in a similar way. This energy is called Qi (pronounced key) by the Japanese and Chi (pronounced chee) by the Chinese. Other cultures throughout the world have many other names for Qi. Examples are Yogic "Prana", Wilheim Reich's "Orgone Energy" and Polynesian "Mana".

Martial artists and healers regard Qi as an actual substance. It is the essence of life, and life cannot continue without it. The word for Qi is also the word for air, but it is a mistake to think of the two as being the same. It is true that good-quality clean air will enhance one's Qi flow, hence the emphasis on breathing techniques by those who study Qigong and other arts such as tantra, Tai Chi and yoga.

Like electricity, Qi cannot normally be seen. Some very advanced adepts have developed the ability to "see" a person's energy field, but these are rare. It can, however, be felt and its effects measured. Later in this book, techniques are explained to help you develop your sensitivity towards Qi. Once you have developed this sensitivity, the Qigong exercises will become more meaningful and you can use them to develop and experiment with your own specific Qi sensitivity.

If you do not wish to accept the idea of Qi, do not feel that you are excluded from working with these techniques. If your reason for not accepting the idea is that you have not been given proof, use the idea as a hypothesis. When your instructor talks about Qi, you can then follow his suggestions without closing yourself to any possibilities. Once you have experimented sufficiently and gathered your own personal data you will be in a position to decide for yourself whether Qi is a useful concept to assist your progress as a healer or martial artist or a "real thing".

Our Qi affects our whole being. Different energy patterns can manifest themselves as different behaviour and health patterns. If we go back to our imagined scenario where we were watching somebody trying to cross a busy pedestrian area, we will have observed a specific energy pattern that predisposes the person to behave in that way. By understanding our own and other people's energy patterns, it becomes possible to devise healing programmes that work for the individual or to avoid situations that drain our resources unnecessarily.

Yin and Yang

If balance is one of our goals, then it follows that we need to balance two opposites. These opposites could be up and down, left and right, fast and slow, internal and external etc. It would therefore be useful to have a generic term for any two opposites. This reduces the requirement for vague phrases such as the "upness" and the "downness" of an entity. The commonly accepted terminology for these opposites are the words "Yin" and "Yang", from the Taoist system of knowledge.

The symbol for this is the well-known Tai Chi symbol. Yin can be regarded as the female and Yang as the male. On the symbol, Yin is the black part and Yang is the white. Other commonly quoted examples are:

Yang	Yin
MALE	FEMALE
LIGHT	DARK
UP	DOWN
LIGHT	HEAVY
EXPANSION	CONTRACTION
HARD	SOFT
LOUD	QUIET
FAST	SLOW
ACTIVE	PASSIVE

Obviously the list could go on forever! There are many subtleties that are much more interesting than trying to compile a definitive list of everything in the Universe that is Yin and Yang. If you were to try and compile such a list, it would show a failure to grasp some of the subtleties as described:-

1 Yin and Yang are Relative and not Absolute. This means that you cannot describe one thing without another to compare it to. A common example is the light and shady side of a hill. The side with the sunlight will be the more Yang side. Now compare the same hill to another where the sun is brighter, and the original Yang will be Yin in relation to the brightness that we are now comparing it with.

2 They are cyclical. Just as day follows night, the calm follows the storm, so Yin will always follow Yang and Yang will always follow Yin

3 Yin will always contain Yang and Yang will always contain Yin. This is shown on our symbol by the white and black dots on either side. A good example of this is that the male sex hormone testosterone will always be present in women whilst all men carry the female sex hormone oestrogen.

Women are generally more Yin than men, but also need Yang energy, just as the Yang male needs Yin energy.

Basically, Yin and Yang are tools that enable us to examine our patterns of movement and thought. Rather than having the vague notion that balance would be a positive thing, the Taoists used these words to describe two opposite polarities. Meditation upon the qualities of Yin and Yang brought further insight into the subtleties of their general nature. These subtleties are encapsulated in the Tai Chi symbol.

The Taoists develop their world view through observations of the Universe. For example, noticing the ways that human behaviour changes between midday and midnight will give an insight into Yin and Yang. These observations need not be limited to Taoist sages. We are all free to make our own observations

Notice how your body relaxes in the warm Yang energy of summer.

Feel how your body "braces itself" on a cold winter's day.

and interpretations. The only premise here is that your observations should be real so that the conclusions that you draw are based on actual information.

Also, remember that if your observations seem at odds to another person's, it does not mean that one of you is wrong. It could just mean that you have uncovered different parts of the same truth.

Tsubos

Many readers of this book will have heard about invisible energy lines or "meridians" that are under the skin and move across your body. If this is true, you will probably know that there are various points along these meridians. These points are locations that an acupuncturist will use to insert a needle. The Japanese name for these points is "Tsubos". A Tsubo is an energy vortex that starts under the skin at the meridian level and expands outwards.

The Japanese symbol for a Tsubo is similar to its actual shape.

If we think back to the analogy of the house and its wiring system, a Tsubo is like an inspection point where you can lift a manhole cover off a drain. If the drain is blocked, then the blockage can be flushed away by a flow of water.

This is the way that some energy healers employ their energetic skills. If energy in a meridian is not flowing sufficiently, then manipulation of Tsubos can alter the flow and release blockages.

Shiatsu makes use of Tsubos, as a way of diagnosing the quality of energy at a point in a meridian or by using the Tsubo directly to invigorate the flow of energy around that point. A therapist who employs techniques such as these will have to develop a high degree of sensitivity in order to be able to feel the changes.

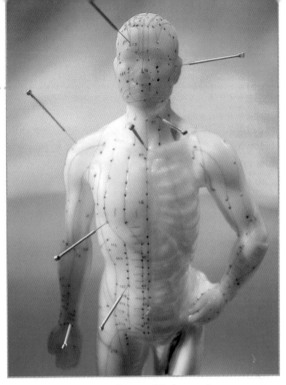

Acupuncturists use meridians and Tsubos to give treatment.

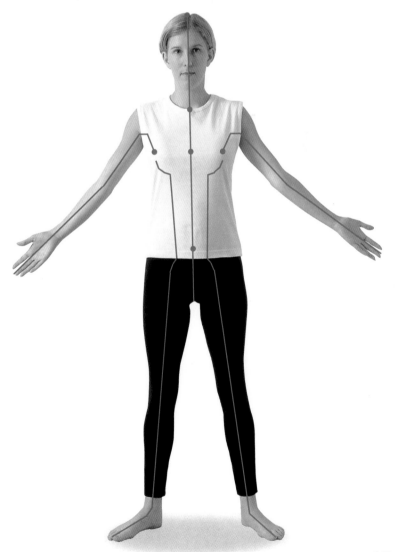

Some methods of Qigong require an elemental knowledge of some Tsubos. This helps to give you a set of internal reference points along which you can sense your energy flow. Even if you cannot yet feel the flow, you will still need to concentrate on the point, as this will increase your awareness and therefore increase your sensitivity to the energy.

Useful Tsubos in Qigong

I remember, in one of my earlier Qigong lessons we were told "Relax and imagine a whirlpool of energy at your Tan Tien". This sounded like an interesting piece of visualisation to me, but I did not have a clue what a "Tan Tien" was.

The Tan Tien (sometimes written Dantian and pronounced Dan-Tee-En) is an important Tsubo in the centre of your abdomen. Most Qigong students do not need to learn all of the Tsubos, their names and locations. There are a few important points that it is a good idea to have a reference for. At least you will be in a situation where you can look up where a point is, if you find yourself in the same situation I was in!

If you know where the following six points are, then you will have the information you need for most lessons. I have included common names for the same points as well as location, description and function. The function is included specifically so that you can practice a little healing work with the points if you are feeling adventurous!

Chinese Name	Translation	Meridian Point	Location	Function
Tan Tien	Original Ki	Conception Vessel 4	2 finger-widths below the navel	Brings energy to the Tan Tien and calms the mind
Yin Tang	Mid Eyebrow	Not applicable	At the mid point of the eyebrows	Stimulates the pituitary gland
Lao Gong	Labour Palace	Pericardium 8	In the middle of the palm between the third and fourth fingers	Draws excess energy away from the heart
Yongchuan	Bubbling Spring	Kidney 1	On the mid line of the foot, $1/3$ distance down from the toes	Stimulates the kidney
Baihui	Hundred Meetings	Governing Vessel 20	At the top of the head on the centre line	Relief for some types of headache
Mingmen	Gate of Life	Governing Vessel 4	Between the second and third lumbar vertebrae	Sexual problems, stimulates kidneys.

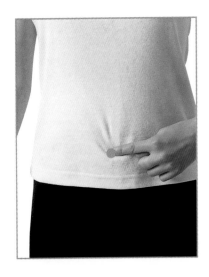

Tan Tien
*Normally the first
point to be taught*

Bai Hui
*This is where all
the Yang energy
finally converges*

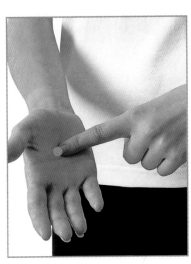

Lao Gong
*This will tingle
during some
exercises*

Ming Men
*Helps the kidneys
stay healthy*

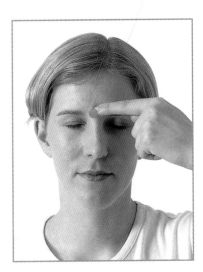

Yin Tang
*Also known as the
"Third Eye" point*

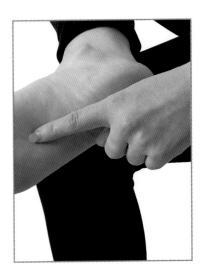

Yong Chuan
*Helps maintain
general vitality*

Qigong and Eastern Thought

The idea of Chi is constant throughout many of the ancient Chinese arts. Seemingly diverse subjects such as calligraphy and interior design are linked by the ever-pervading world of Chi. In Chinese calligraphy, the same principles apply as in Qigong, that is, that the whole body should be relaxed and moving as one piece to create truly artful calligraphy. If you were to design or decorate a building, it would be normal to consult a Feng Shui consultant.

Many of the ideas that are traditionally linked to the concept of Chi, can also be interpreted by the Westerner as common sense. For example, office Feng Shui tends to create a positive working environment. I think, however, that this would be missing the point that trying to be harmonious with the Universe generally creates positive effects, provided that the intent is good.

Three areas that have been linked to the concept of Chi from the early days are philosophy, martial arts and healing. These three areas have been so closely linked with the notion of Chi, that they are worthy of further consideration.

Chi and Philosophy

Ancient philosophical works such as the Tao Te Ching dated around 240 BC by the Taoist Sage Lao Tzu were highly influenced by the concept of Chi. Their deep meditations and close contact with nature provided them with boundless inspiration for their writings.

For example, in chapter 42 of the Tao Te Ching, Lao Tzu writes:

"Tao gave birth to one; the one gave birth to two. The two gave birth to the ten thousand things."

This is a description of how Yin and Yang were created from the Tao and subsequently Yin and Yang are the creators of the many things in the Universe.

From the same chapter:

"It is on the blending of the breaths that the harmony depends."

This gives us a poetic idea of balancing energies or "breaths" to create harmony. It also gives a direct reference to the idea of breathing. Breathing, as you will see later is an important part of all Qigong exercises. The Chinese character for Chi is also the character for breath, which further emphasises the point.

Qigong and Martial Arts

As any martial artist will know, there is much more to their art than meets the eye. A true martial art will develops the practitioner's spirit rather than simply offering a sophisticated way of beating somebody up!

So, with this thought in mind, the aim of traditional martial arts is more to develop a strong spirit than to teach the "Kung Fu Death Touch" or other such legendary techniques. If the development of a strong spirit is the goal for martial arts, then martial arts share a similar goal to Qigong.

martial arts' masters throughout the ages have obviously not missed this point. Indeed, a common story about the origins of Tai Chi (a soft-style martial art) is that the style comes from Taoist monks who needed to develop their meditation and energy practices into a martial art. The reason was that they needed to defend themselves against bandits. The story may or may not be true. It is a fact that many martial arts' masters also have a highly developed knowledge of the philosophies related to their art and a healing art that employs the use of energy.

Qigong was and is an integral part of all martial arts' styles. It may not always be termed Qigong, but the same concepts will be employed. The most common examples are the conscious flow of energy coupled with an understanding of the Yin and Yang used in Tai Chi. The famous demonstrations by the Shaolin monks, where solid objects are broken against a person's body employ a "hard" style of Qigong.

In the styles of martial art that are not traditionally associated with Qigong and energy-building practices, the concepts are still involved. For example, the Judo player will try to keep his body relaxed and alert, so that he can flow with the movements of his partner and thus try to gain an advantage. Also try to imagine a Tae Kwon Do or Karate student who did not show strong spirit – his teacher or Sensei would probably regard them as "work in progress".

Qigong exercises can help the martial artist stay strong and supple.

Qigong focusses the mind - a vital skill for the martial artist.

Qigong and the Healing Arts

Qigong and meditation take the practitioner on an inward exploration of the self that is akin to the Shamanistic traditions.

The tools that Qigong provide allow one to directly influence the energy in the body's organs and meridians. It has to be remembered here, that the word "organ" in this context is further-reaching than in the standard medical texts of the West. Each organ is an important energy centre and will have specific emotions and thoughts that are influenced by it. For example, a familiar example for us are the thoughts and emotions that are connected to the heart, e.g. love and joyfulness.

Qigong is a set of movements and meditations that will affect these energy patterns. It therefore has several uses to the healer.

1 Self Development. Before you can try to help another person to heal himself, you need to be in fairly good shape yourself. For this reason alone, many healers will practice Qigong, Tai Chi or similar exercises.

2 Learning. This is especially true for the trainee healer. Some exercises will work on a specific organ or meridian. This allows the trainee to feel for himself the effect of working with that particular energy.

3 Diagnostic. The fact that an exercise will emphasise the use of a particular meridian gives an indicator to its energetic state. For example, the gallbladder meridian runs along the side of your body. If you find side stretches painful, you may have a weakness in that meridian. As with any other diagnostic tool, it should not be used in isolation – it should be correlated with other factors such as facial diagnosis.

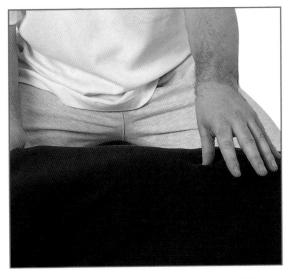

Qigong assists the healer in improving his or her sensitivity to energy flow.

4 Prescriptive. If a healer finds a weakness in a certain meridian or set of meridians, they may recommend certain Qigong exercises to help boost the energy in the weakness and therefore assist healing. This is a powerful technique as it forces the client to become more involved with his own healing.

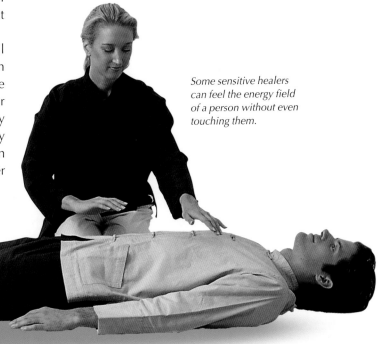

Some sensitive healers can feel the energy field of a person without even touching them.

Types of Qigong

If you ever visit a major city in the Far East, such as Tokyo or Beijing, there is a good chance that you will encounter different Qigong teachers and healers. Many will be offering a system of working that is claimed to be "different from the others" and the "best". As Qigong becomes more popular in the West, I have witnessed Qigong "masters" who seem to have better marketing skills than Qigong techniques.

The range of different styles of Qigong is partly responsible for this situation. It is difficult to compare two different "masters" who claim to have totally different skills. For example, some healers claim the ability to heal from a great distance or even over the telephone and others claim great martial skill from their Qigong practice.

When asked for a demonstration you may hear lines like "such demonstrations are too crass for our school" or "the technique is so dangerous that it could kill you". A very common way of hiding a lack of skill can be to charge large amounts of money for the lessons!

However, there are also many genuine, very skilled individuals for you to find. It is sometimes difficult for the uninitiated to decide what is good and what is a waste of time and money. The main advice that I would give here is to follow your instincts, but always to question them. If a teacher seems to have what you are looking for, give them a try. If later you find that you were mistaken, there is no harm in the fact that you tried them out.

If you have a basic knowledge of some of the Qigong concepts, you will be more able to discriminate the good teachers from the not-so-good. The following is a general description of the different types of Qigong. The aim at this point is to give a general overview, so that most Qigong styles fit the description.

Qigong that uses Intent

To move Qi, you need to use your mind. If you can focus your mind into a certain part of your body, you will start to feel different sensations such as warmth or tingling. If you can move that focus, then the warmth or tingling will also move.

This focus is given the name "intent". By learning how to focus your intent, you will learn how to feel energy. By learning how to move your intent, you will learn how to move energy.

An analogy that appeals to my training in engineering is that intent is similar to the voltage that makes current flow through an electrical circuit.

Examples of the use of intent are the Karate expert who can break blocks by punching "beyond" the object and the healer who can make their hands feel "warm and tingling" by using intent.

Intent is a powerful tool that can help you to unlock the secrets of Qigong. You should always try to maintain a balanced approach, rather than trying too hard to feel a certain point.

Intent should be relaxed but focussed.

Qigong that does not use Intent

Another mode of thought is that the mind should be inactive during practice. The practitioner's mind should be tranquil and relaxed.

This is the mental opposite to the focus employed when you use intent. The advantage of this style is that you do not filter out any messages that your body is trying to send you that you were not necessarily seeking.

This approach uses a concept that is frequently referred to as "Wu Wei". The term Wu Wei is sometimes mistaken for "doing nothing". A better way of thinking about Wu Wei is doing nothing that is not required. This includes trying to alter something that was perfectly good in the first place, or constantly talking about what you are doing with your mind, so that you are distracted from achieving your goals.

Very few Qigong styles will be exclusively one thing or another. It is more common to find a style that balances the intent with no-mind.

Most styles of Qigong will comprise of one or more of the following elements:-

Standing Qigong

The most common form of standing Qigong is the exercise "Standing Like a Tree", and is covered in greater detail later in the book. Standing Qigong is very good for developing internal and external strength. It emphasises the use of correct posture and teaches you how to stay in a strong posture. The static nature of the exercise makes it ideal for developing mental and physical stamina.

Standing Qigong is an example of something that looks easy but is deceptively difficult. The newcomer to standing Qigong will quickly grasp the idea of how it works and then develop the strength and inner quiet to hold the position for a time. Do not be disheartened if you find it difficult in the beginning. I have seen advanced athletes who find it difficult at the start! Normally, after a few weeks practice, you will feel the difference.

Let the movement relax your body so that the energy can flow.

Standing like a tree.

Flowing Qigong

Many of the Qigong forms involve some sort of flowing movement. Some of these are described later. This form is excellent for helping to correct structural problems and improving the health of your joints.

The movements should flow naturally, as Taoist theory would predict. This helps you to unwind any stiffness in your body and become more supple. The movements are also designed to "pump" energy through the meridians and thus keep the organs healthy.

Generally, flowing Qigong is less physically demanding than standing Qigong, so it is introduced at an earlier stage. It is still important to maintain good posture but will be more difficult if you are moving. To help you keep your body straight and feel any changes the exercises are normally done slowly. It will normally take a couple of weeks to notice a difference from when you first start your lessons.

Movement should be fluid so that the energy can flow smoothly.

Meditative Qigong

Meditation has proved to be very effective for stress relief. As stress is the "hidden killer" of our time, meditation seems to be an invaluable tool. It can also help with your concentration and clarity of mind – also useful skills.

When we talk about meditation in Qigong, there is usually an active part of the mind that is thinking about energy. You may be working with an energy circuit as in the microcosmic orbit described later or simply be meditating and focussing on your Tan Tien or some other point.

There are other styles of meditation that call for the practitioner to strive towards a "no mind" state (for example). Try a few different methods and see which you like the best.

The Holistic Body

Where is your mind? Think about the question for a moment and find your own answer. You may be of the opinion that your brain houses your mind, but what about your personality and emotions? These are questions that are quite difficult to answer, probably because words like "mind", "emotions" and "personality" can also vary slightly in their definition. A neurologist will probably have different answers to these questions to an acupuncturist. The fact that the answers are different does not mean that one of them is wrong, only that the two professions tend to think in different ways.

Qigong uses a holistic image of the body. The idea that the whole is greater than the sum of the parts is important here. The model adopts the notion that, ideally, all parts of the body should work in harmony with each other for optimum health. When we say "all parts", we mean the mind, body and spirit and all their various components.

A relaxed body helps to nurture a stress-free state of mind.

Learning to relax can reduce or eliminate the need for sleeping pills.

An example of this could be a person who has trouble sleeping. To solve the problem, a short-term answer could be to take sleeping pills. This would address the effect of the problem but not the cause.

A holistic approach would be to investigate the cause of the insomnia, which might easily be stress. In our example, the stress was being caused by a situation where the sufferer felt that they were lacking a dimension in their life that made it feel meaningful – a common affliction in busy modern life!

Obviously, sleeping pills would only mask the feelings and allow them to resurface again at some point in the future. If our sufferer were to learn some meditation techniques, it would help them to relax and therefore aid restful sleep. Another effect of meditation is that is gives you a greater mental capacity to explore your inner feelings. If the sufferer can find the root of the anxiety, then he or she will have made the first step towards doing something about it.

Please remember that the above is purely an example, if you are having trouble sleeping, meditation may help but you may need to consult a practitioner for advice.

In Chinese medicine, anger is believed to cause injury to the liver.

Stress can cause insomnia, which depletes the energy and causes more stress.

Energetic Body Language

We all understand different aspects of body language. Some people will have made a specific study of the subject. If you are not one of them, you will still have an in-built understanding of the subject – we all know what an angry person looks like!

In Qigong theory, mind and body communication is a two-way process. This means that if you are manifesting body language that indicates anger, it is possible to alter the emotions that cause the anger by altering your body.

This may sound slightly fanciful, but try it – it works. Next time you are feeling depressed, try observing your body posture. Typically, you will find that your head is bowed and your body is slumped. In Qigong terms, your spirit is weak at that moment.

Depression gives you the feeling that your energy has "collapsed". Qigong can help you to lift your spirits.

Try lifting up your head and straightening your back. Take a deep breath, open your eyes and allow yourself to SMILE. This body language will feed itself straight back to your mind. It is normally enough to start to lift a person's spirits for a short time. The problem that caused the depression may still be there, but at least you feel a little better about yourself for a while.

Later in the book, a smiling meditation is described in more detail (see page 106). Remember, a simple smile is enough to raise your spirits. Conversely, if you have a strong spirit, it is easy to smile!

A good smile can indicate good health.

Breathing

Do you know how you breathe? Assuming that you know how to breathe (not breathing would make reading this book difficult!), you need to pay attention to how you breathe. It has already been mentioned that breathing is central to any energy exercises. The word Chi is actually interchangeable with the word breath.

The Taoist idea is that the lungs not only take in air from the environment, but on a more subtle level, they take in Chi from the environment as well. The Chi is taken in during respiration and distributed throughout the body. This function is also closely related to the function of the heart and brain. Considering this, it is easy to see how breathing also plays such an important role in Qigong and other disciplines such as Yoga.

Yoga will teach deep breathing.

So what is the big idea about breathing? We all breathe, or else we die. Hopefully, the next few pages will help you to understand the ideas linking breathing and Chi. When you start the actual exercises, you will then be able to understand a little more of how they work and what they are trying to achieve.

How Do You Breathe?

Try the following exercise to learn whether you breathe from your chest or stomach.

1 Sit quietly for a minute or so.
2 Make your breathing quite deep and long in duration.
3 Place your hands over your navel.
4 If your hands are stationary, then you are breathing using your chest.
5 If your hands move with the rhythm of your breathing, you are practising abdominal breathing.

Abdominal breathing is deeper and more relaxed. It allows more oxygen and Chi to circulate in your body and is therefore central to most Qigong exercises. If you found that your breathing was more in the chest DO NOT PANIC! Many Qigong students reach the point where they understand the difference between abdominal breathing and chest breathing. Upon finding out that they breathe with the chest, the next step seems to be to force themselves to breathe with the abdomen. However, forcing the change will cause more harm than good.

You have already made the first step, which is awareness. Now, through your practice of Qigong, your awareness will increase. When your body is ready, you will start to breathe abdominally without making any effort. This is the way it should be, remember that you cannot force changes with the Tao, you should always "follow the flow".

Gentle practice is the key to success. I find that a good place to practise abdominal breathing is when I am sitting in my car at traffic lights.

1 – 2

3 – 5

Relaxation and "Fight or Flight"

The nervous system is made up of two parts, the somatic and autonomic systems. The somatic system can be under our conscious control. It gathers information from our sense organs and transmits signals to our muscles to allow movement.

The autonomic system is under our unconscious control. It is mainly concerned with the automatic functions of the body such as breathing and heartbeat. The autonomic system is divided into two parts known as the parasympathetic and the sympathetic.

When you are relaxed, the parasympathetic nervous system is dominant. Your breathing is deep and muscles relaxed. When your body is in the "parasympathetic mode", you can digest food, make love and your body can heal itself.

The sympathetic mode is the "fight or flight" mode. Adrenalin pumps through your body, you are alert and ready to run or fight. Obviously, activities such as eating or making love will be unimportant if you are deciding whether to run or fight for your life.

A major problem for many people is that they become "stuck" in the fight or flight mode. Imagine that a driver nearly runs you off the road on your way to work. Your nervous system puts you into the fight or flight mode. You arrive at work and plunge yourself into more stress, to keep you going you drink coffee throughout the day. The effect of these actions will put you into the fight or flight mode for the whole of the day and well into the evening.

The effect of this imbalance can be disturbed sleep, poor digestion, weak breathing and sexual problems.

If there were a way of making sure that your body was able to switch back into the relaxation mode, better balance would

be achieved. This can help to break the cycle of stress that is causing the problems.

Exercises such as Qigong, meditation and Tai Chi are very effective at helping your body to switch its mode to relaxation. Add to this the fact that exercise can help to detoxify your system and over time you may start to feel that you have more energy and a more positive outlook on life!

Qigong teaches you how to control your "fight or flight" mode.

Breathing and the Emotions

In Taoism, there is an idea of "letting go" of what you no longer require. The Taoist sage would be the type of person who has let go of many of the materialist items in life. Externally, the life of the sage appears to be a very simple one, with no computers or televisions or sophisticated modern conveniences.

We do not all need to become sages and dispose of our worldly goods to benefit from the idea of letting go. It is, however, a healthy thing to be able to do on an emotional level. The classic example here is the idea of grieving for the loss of a loved one. After a period of grief, the bereaved must be able to let go of the person. The memories and love for the person are still there, but it is the grieving that one must try to release.

On a more mundane and everyday level, if somebody gives you a bad time, it is helpful to be able to let go of the hurt that they have caused. If you cling to the emotions and anger that the person has stirred up in you, it can make you unhappy and even ill.

The organ that is most connected to these emotions is the lung. It is ruled by the metal element from Five Element Theory. The metal element is intrinsically connected with the idea of disposing of what you do not need.

The physical function of the lung is respiration. During inhalation, we take in fresh air and Chi. On exhalation we let go of carbon dioxide and make room for fresh Chi. It is fairly common for a person not to release all the carbon dioxide during breathing. This will shorten the length of the breath and make breathing less efficient.

On an emotional level, the person with the weak exhalation may be being blocked by an unwillingness to let go of emotions that are no longer helpful to us.

Breathing exercises from Qigong will cause subtle changes in this cycle. The exercises will teach your physical body how to let go of unwanted carbon dioxide. This will uplift your emotions from the better availability of fresh air and Chi to your body.

Your body can then begin to notice the difference on an unconscious level and also know what has caused the difference. This is a reason why many people feel very positive effects from their first Qigong or similar lessons.

Wood

Fire

Earth

Metal

Water

Gut Reactions

Have you ever had butterflies in the stomach or felt lovesick? Many people experience sensations in their abdomen when under stress or extreme emotional conditions.

This is not surprising if you are accustomed to thinking about energy. In energetic terms, the abdomen, or Hara, as it is also known, is an important energy centre for your body. Each time that you get a feeling in your abdominal area such as fear or love, the energy is being affected.

In Taoist theory, if two things share similar appearances, they are also likely to have energetic patterns that resonate with each other. An example is the kidney bean, which is said by many therapists to be good for your kidneys, because of the energy that it contains.

If you imagine a human brain and a human gut, there are similar visual appearances. In energetic terms, this means that there will be other similarities and resonances. Some Taoists actually refer to the gut as a "second brain". The upper brain is then concerned with thinking and the lower brain is concerned with instinct.

This is consistent with the Japanese idea of Hara. If a warrior understands how to use Hara, they will act on a more instinctive level. This will be quicker and more deadly than the person who has to process a set of thoughts through their mind before acting. The healer will also use Hara, but obviously to preserve life rather than end it!

A task for both the warrior or healer is to be able to use their Hara or second brain. This will unleash energy and instinctual vitality.

The first part of this process is to learn abdominal breathing, as it brings more oxygen and energy to your Hara. Following that, exercises from the Qigong set will help you to establish a better connection.

The Hara is located in the abdomen and is vitally important in Qigong.

Posture and Stances

One aim of Qigong is the development and reinforcement of spirit. Few people will decide to follow the life of a monk to develop spirit, but that does not exclude them from spiritual development. Qigong can be an excellent tool for this work.

Many people who start learning Qigong already understand that it is connected to work of this nature. Many modern lives seem to have lacked a spiritual dimension for years. After a while some people become aware of this missing element in their lives and decide to embark on a course such as Qigong or Tai Chi.

This decision is a good one, as the right teacher may indeed be able to help. There is, however, a risk. For this work, the student has to realise that the first thing that they need to work on is body, not spirit. If a Qigong teacher were to start immediately working on the spiritual dimension of Qigong, the lessons would be at best meaningless and at worst possibly dangerous.

Working with the body gives you a strong foundation and helps release energy blockages. This process may take years to perfect, but remember that every adjustment that your physical body makes is always echoed by your energy body, so you are actually working on all levels without knowing it!

The first physical entity that requires attention is posture. A good posture will keep you grounded and stable. Later, we will explore static standing postures. These will help develop great stamina and strength in your body. For now, it is important to learn why we need to understand posture to give us a good foundation to work from.

Your posture should be comfortable to you and not cause strain to any of your joints. Some schools require you to hold different postures for a fairly long time. This will give you good grounding, but can damage your knees if your body is not ready for it.

The postures that we will cover here are common to Qigong and to Tai Chi. There are four basic postures, all of which are developments from the original Wu Chi posture.

1. The Wu Chi Posture

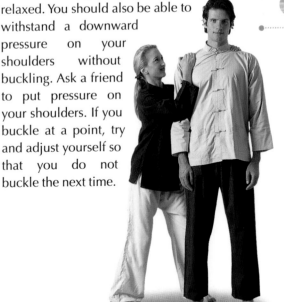

Wu Chi, in Taoist cosmology is the nothing from which the Universe was born. As such, the Wu Chi posture represents the idea of nothingness. In all of the other postures, there are echoes of the Wu Chi posture, just as there are echoes of the original Wu Chi throughout the Universe.

1 Stand with your feet shoulder-width apart. Make the inner edges of your feet parallel. Straighten, but do not lock, your knees. Straighten your back (tuck your pelvis in slightly). Drop your shoulders. Drop your chin and lift the crown of your head. Look forwards, but do not allow anything to grab your attention. Relax your breathing.

2 When you finish, your back should be straight and your joints relaxed. You should also be able to withstand a downward pressure on your shoulders without buckling. Ask a friend to put pressure on your shoulders. If you buckle at a point, try and adjust yourself so that you do not buckle the next time.

2. Parallel Stance

If you managed the Wu Chi posture, the parallel stance will be easy. Do not be confused by their similarity. The difference is that you hold your weight lower in the parallel stance, so that you can control your movement.

1 Stand in the Wu Chi posture.
2 Bend your knees slightly as though you were resting your buttock on the edge of a chair. Keep your back straight.
3 Test this posture by having a friend push you from the side. You should be able to withstand a strong push before they can topple you.

3. Bow Stance

This is a very stable stance for moving forwards and is popular in nearly all martial arts. Some styles will have slight modifications, but the basic idea will be similar.

1 Stand in the Wu Chi posture.
2 Turn your right foot to a 45 degree angle. Sink your weight on to your right leg. Step forwards with your left leg. Your left shin should be perpendicular to the floor, your right leg straight but not locked and your back straight. Your weight distribution should be 70% on your front leg and 30% on your back leg.
3 This stance is very strong if somebody tries to push you back. See how much pressure you can withstand before your friend can move you.

4. Empty Stance

Empty stance is another upright stance. Physically, it is the most difficult stance, because all of your weight is on one leg.

1 Stand in the Wu Chi posture.

2 Turn your right foot to a 45 degree angle.

3 Sink your weight on to your right leg. Move your left leg to a position where your heels are in line with each other. Keep all of your weight on your right leg, so that the left leg is "empty".

4 This will be difficult to hold for long when you are a beginner. Test the posture by having a friend pull your arm towards them. If they can topple you forwards, you need to develop your stance more. Do not rush, because it will take some time to gain the strength in your standing leg to hold the stance.

Qigong Guidelines

In Qigong, various teachers have outlined sets of rules or guidelines to try to help their students obtain maximum benefit from their exercises. If you were to look through enough books, you might eventually reach a point where you would not be able to practice any Qigong if you attempted to adhere to all the different guidelines.

There are various reasons for this, such as misinterpretation of original information and even the information being wrong in the first place. From attending many seminars and learning with high level teachers, I have come to the conclusion that there are only two major rules that should be followed. These are:

> **1** If it hurts STOP.
> **2** The body postures should be comfortable throughout the practice.

There are other elements that may be taken into consideration to obtain the best results from your practice.

Breathing

Breathing is normally done through the nose with the mouth gently shut. The tongue should touch the roof of your mouth.

Mind

Depending on how you are practising, your mind should be either focussed on your intent or empty. Try not to be distracted by irrelevant thoughts such as what you are going to have for dinner.

Food

Some teachers say that you should not practise unless your stomach is empty. I think that this can be limiting, because it means that your practising time is severely limited. If I know that I need to eat less than two hours before a practice session, I just eat a lighter meal. This may not be as good as having an empty stomach – but it is better than having a full one!

Also, it can be distracting to try and exercise if you are hungry. You will be trying to fix your intent on the movement that you are doing, and it will wander to your next meal.

Environment

Try to pick a place that is light and airy. This will enhance the natural Chi in the air. Practising outdoors is a good experience, but try to find a place where you will not attract too much attention, otherwise you are very likely to be distracted.

If you are a traveller, then there is nothing to stop you practising in your hotel room. Indeed, it could be just what your body needs after long hours seated on a plane or in a car. Try to let fresh air into the room if you can, but the chances are that anything that you do will be beneficial.

Health

If you are unsure about the suitability of the exercises, you should consult your doctor or therapist. Generally speaking, the exercises will be beneficial to your health but if you are in any doubt, always check first.

Clothing

There is no set uniform for Qigong. The exercise should not put strain on any part of your body, so you will not need any protective gear. You will need to ensure that your clothes are loose-fitting and light, so that they do not restrict your movements. There is nothing to stop you practising Qigong naked, but keep away from the window or draw the curtains!

How Much?

This will be explained further in "Setting a

Training Schedule", but the most important point is to observe the first rule, "if it hurts, stop". This also includes the mental pain of trying to make your body repeat a movement so many times that you become bored with it. It is important that you should enjoy your practice.

Setting a Training Schedule

The only way that Qigong can work for you is if you practise it. I have seen many people who have a good theoretical understanding of Qigong and Tai Chi, but very little real skill. These are the people who enjoy talking about the art, rather than actually doing it.

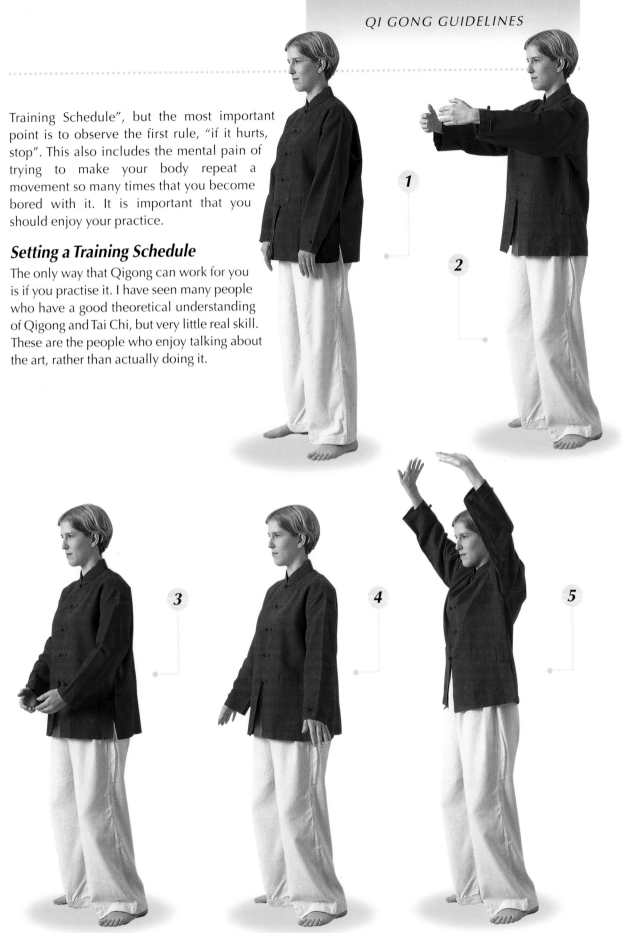

For real results, you need to train frequently. Start by training every other day. As you begin to learn and understand the exercises, it will be easier for you to train every day. If you train little and often in this way, you will gain more benefit than from having one long training session in a week.

In the early days, do not try to do too much. If you can train for 15–30 minutes every other day, you will soon start to reap the rewards. Try to incorporate the exercises that you are practising into your daily schedule.

If you have trouble falling asleep, try the "Onion Skin" meditation. If you can make time in the morning, try a few gentle movements and the "Inner Smile" meditation. It could alter your daytime mood so much that your work mates will wonder at your secret!

If you are feeling stressed from a hard day, try some of the flowing movements to loosen your body. Follow the flowing movements with some standing Qigong and meditation, and your workplace will seem like a completely different part of your life, rather than invading your home life.

If you really want to learn about Qigong, you will need to learn much about yourself and your inner workings. One of the best ways to do this is to keep a logbook or diary. In it, record all that YOU think important for your progress in Qigong. It may start with what exercises you have done, but can go where you want it. You may record your feelings, emotions, dreams and health and so on, the choice is yours!

For the absolute beginner, the following is a typical list of exercises and time taken for a 30-minute routine.

1. WARM UPS	5 MINUTES
2. FLOWING MOVEMENT	10 MINUTES
3. STANDING QIGONG	5 MINUTES
4. STRETCHING QIGONG	5 MINUTES
5. MEDITATION	5 MINUTES

For the warm ups, try to go through the whole of your body, from head to toe. Then pick any of the flowing, standing, stretching and meditation exercises that you want for your session. If you vary your selections from day to day, you will learn what all of the exercises do for your body and be less prone to boredom.

When this becomes too easy, simply select harder exercises or increase the length of your training session.

Warm Ups

The major cause of injury in Qigong is lack of proper warm-up exercises. The fittest of athletes are very aware that they need to warm up before practising their skill. Presuming that you are not in this small percentage, the need for warming up is even more crucial.

Many of the Qigong movements look like warm-up exercises in themselves. It is true that some martial arts' instructors use Qigong as part of their warm-up routine, that these exercises can be used in such a way. Remember that martial artists tend to be very fit in the first place, and they will always start with the easy exercises to loosen the body.

In the beginning, it is recommended to have a set of exercises that you know and learn as warm-up exercises. The following sequence is just such a set.

The routine starts from the top of the body and works its way down to the feet and is completed by some basic stretches. If you are warming up specifically for stretching exercises, you may wish to omit these exercises in favour of the stretching routine described later in this book (see pages 55–57).

Each of the exercises should be done for a minimum of one minute. Ideally, you should spend more time on warm ups, say two to three minutes on each exercise. If you only have 30 minutes in which to practise, then you need to cut down the times and be a little more careful.

The warm-up exercises are also good for isolating a particular joint for exercise. For example, if you know that you have stiff shoulders, the shoulder rotations are an ideal choice.

When performing any of these exercises, it is important to "listen" to your body. If an exercise is painful, then your body is objecting to it. You should either ease off on the exercise, or leave it out completely. This is especially true with neck rotations, as the neck can be a very delicate area.

Exercise 1 - shaking and breathing

1 Start in the Wu Chi posture. Begin by shaking the fingertips. This need not be particularly vigorous. It is to start to bring some movement into the body. As you breathe in, imagine that you are also breathing in pure energy. Imagine the energy travelling to your fingertips. Feel each of your fingertips as you move them and fill each of them with energy.

2 When you can "feel into" each fingertip, move your attention further up the finger into the first joint. Imagine that, as you breathe Chi in through the lungs, the joint becomes more relaxed. Carry on doing this exercise for all of the joints in the hand, working inwards from the fingertips up to the wrist. Notice how we have moved the intent from the fingertips through the hand. The hands should feel more relaxed by now.

3 Continue with the exercise, gradually moving your attention from the wrist through to the forearm and elbow. Allow the elbow to loosen, and start to move the biceps and tricep muscles at the top of the arm. To finish, shake the shoulders up and down, letting the arms hang free.

4 Allow the movement to gradually slow down and stop. Now carry out exactly the same exercise with your legs. Put your weight into your left leg and start to shake the toes of your right leg. Gradually move the intent through the toes, foot and ankle.

5 Then move onto the lower leg and knee.

6 Finally shake out the thigh. You will also find that this is good exercise for balancing on the standing leg.

When you have shaken the tension away from the right leg, repeat the exercise with the left leg.

Exercise 2 – neck rotations

Tension in the neck can cause Chi stagnation that may lead to headaches. Neck rotations can allow the neck to become freer and allow better flow of Chi.

1 Start by standing in the Wu Chi posture.
2 Lift the crown of your head slightly to extend through the neck. Do not strain. Look upwards with your eyes.
3 Imagine that you are drawing a circle with your eyes. Move the head around in a circle to try and make the biggest circle that you can with your eyes. Make the movement slow, so that you do not

pull the neck and so that you can co-ordinate the breathing with it.
4 When you feel the neck has become looser, stop the movement and repeat in the opposite direction.

Do not be alarmed at the crackling noise that the neck can make. It is partly caused by releasing tension from the neck.

This exercise is done with the back straight and the shoulders down. A common error is to try and make the biggest circle possible by moving the back with the neck.

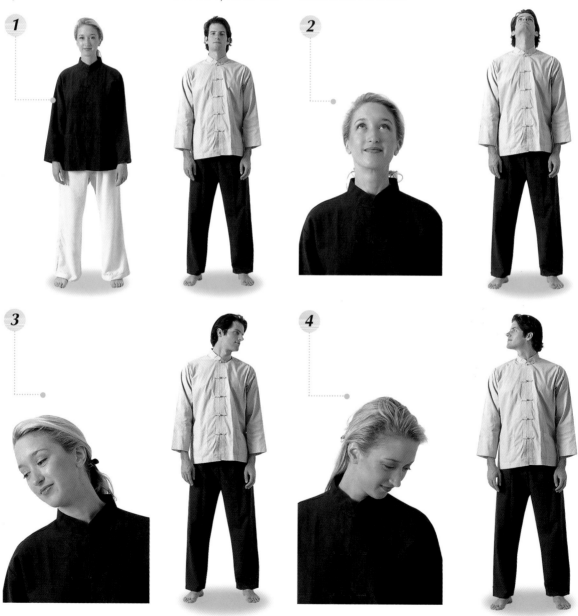

Exercise 3 - shoulder rotations

The shoulders are very sensitive to energy changes within the body. If a person is sick, Traditional Chinese Medicine can diagnose it in the shoulders.

1 Start by standing in the Wu Chi posture.
2 On an inward breath, lift the shoulders. Time the lifting of the shoulders to synchronise with the inward breath. When the lungs are full and the shoulders are lifted to their maximum point, slowly allow the breath out and let the shoulders descend.
3 Repeat the movement several times, and then change the direction of the shoulder rotation. Try to do the movement quite slowly, so that it is easier to time the movement of the shoulders with the movement of the breath.

4 Keep the back straight and the head up. Do not allow the knees to become locked. This will allow you to feel the movement throughout the whole of your body, rather than just isolated within the shoulder area.

Try to complete approximately the same number of repetitions of the exercise in both directions of rotation. The movement should be repeated enough times to allow the shoulders to become looser. In the beginning, ten to fifteen rotations in either direction will normally make a difference. When your body is used to the exercise, it is better to feel how many rotations you need to do rather than stick to numbers.

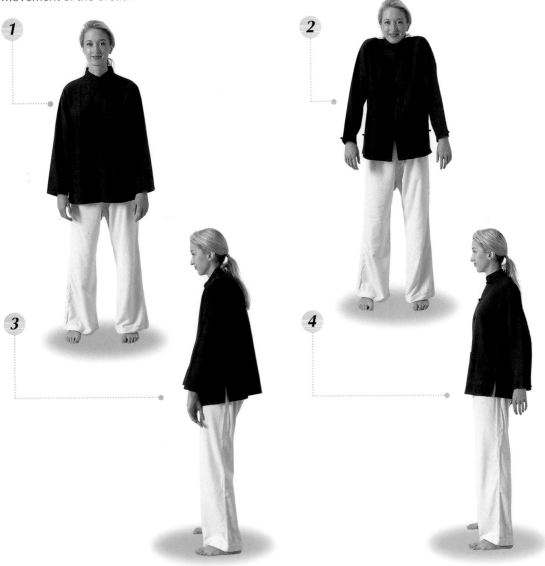

Exercise 4 - waist rotations

In Tai Chi, the waist must be free to move. This exercise also massages the kidney area and the important energy points for the kidneys.

1 Start by standing in the Wu Chi position.

2 Place the palms of the hands on the kidney area. Feel the warmth of the hands on your lower back. Visualise the warmth penetrating and surrounding the kidneys.

3 Start to make small circles with the waist. The circles will start small, but gradually increase in size. The waist will be moving in an outward spiral. Keep the breathing relaxed. Do not over stretch and keep the feet flat on the floor.

4 When you have reached the maximum size of rotation, carry on and repeat the waist rotations until the waist feels noticeably looser. When you have completed several rotations, start to spiral the waist back to the centre. The waist should spiral out to the maximum rotation and then spiral back in to the stationary position. Never try to reach the extreme of the movement on the first circle or suddenly stop when you have reached the extreme.

When you reach the rest position, repeat the waist rotations in the other direction. Repeat the same number of rotations in both directions.

Beginners should be able to perform fifteen to twenty rotations.

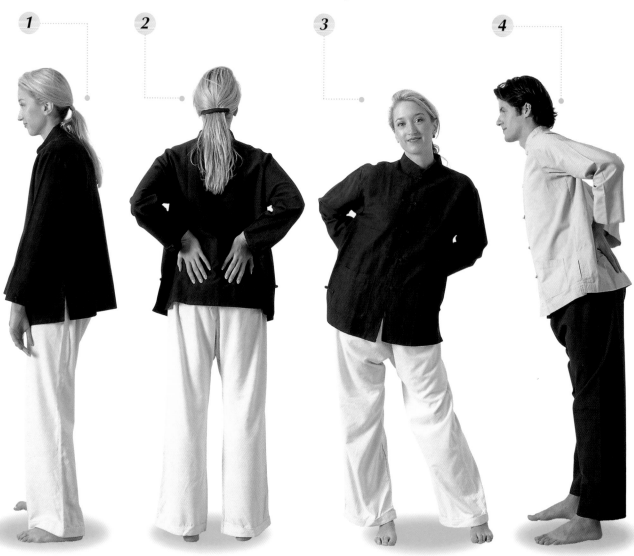

1   *2*   *3*   *4*

Exercise 5 – moving the waist and swinging the arms

This exercise invigorates the flow of Chi throughout the whole of the body and teaches you movement from the Tan Tien.

1 Stand in the Wu Chi posture.
2 Oscillate to the left and the right. While you are moving the waist to the left and right, keep the body straight and the arms relaxed. Start quite slowly, but gradually build up speed. Do not become too vigorous with the movements, otherwise it will be difficult to keep the correct movements. You can, however, exert some effort into the exercise if you wish.

This movement is similar to all of the other Tai Chi exercises because there is more happening with the exercise than is initially apparent. To the untrained observer this exercise looks as if you are simply swinging the arms. The arms in actual fact do very little but remain relaxed for the exercise.

The lift for the arms comes from the rotation of the waist. As the waist rotates about an axis, a physical force lifts the arms. Do not try to simply swing the arms otherwise you will miss the point of the exercise.

3 In the beginning the arms should swing around the waist. This gives a massage to the lower abdomen and the kidney area of the back.

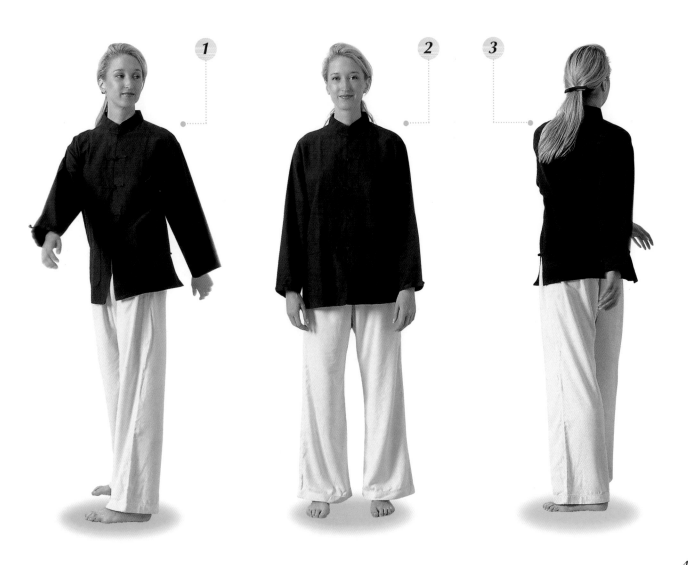

When you have been practising this exercise for a number of weeks, you will have learned how to "let go" of the arms and let them swing with the body. When you have trained your body to this level, you can use the exercise to massage the torso and the neck, rather than just the lower areas.

4 Do this simply by swinging the arms higher. You can throw the hand over the shoulder or work higher with the neck if you desire.

5 Do not do this too hard, especially when massaging the neck, or you may hurt yourself. Be sure to keep the shoulders down even if you are working high on the body.

When you have had enough, let the waist momentum gradually slow down and stop. Do not try to stop suddenly because this can lead to injury.

Exercise 6 - knee rotations

Keeping the knees healthy and loose will help to prevent arthritis. There are many acupuncture points around the knees that benefit from this exercise.

Note: Do not attempt this exercise if you have any problems with your knees or if you feel discomfort.

1 Stand with both feet together and the ankles touching. Bend the knees slightly and reach down to rest the palms of your hands on your kneecaps.
2 Make small circles with the knees. Allow the circles to gradually increase in size. Do not try to make the knee circles too large (especially as a beginner) as this can strain the knee.
When you have made several circles in one direction, slow down and stop. Then repeat the exercise a similar number of times in the opposite direction.

When you first try this exercise, keep the number of knee rotations low. This will reduce any risk of knee strain. Five or ten repetitions will be plenty in the early stages. When you have learned how the knee performs with the exercise and gained experience of it, you can increase the number of rotations.

The exercise is performed with the feet flat on the floor. You may feel that your balance is slightly wobbly in the beginning. This is improved by focussing the eyes on a point on the floor. The point should be static and approximately one metre away. This gives you a reference point and makes the movement more stable.

1

2

Exercise 7 - ankle rotations

Tension in the ankle joint will cause the movement to be less grounded. Rotations of the ankle can help release the tension and enhance the feeling of grounding.

Stand in the Wu Chi posture. Lift the heel of the right foot from the floor so that the only part of the foot touching the floor is the big toe. Keep the leg relaxed and the toe in the same position on the floor. Rotate the knee in a clockwise direction. Start with small rotations and build up to larger ones. Keeping the toe fixed and the knee rotating will cause the most movement in the ankle.

After ten to twenty rotations, slow down to a stop. Repeat the exercise with an anticlockwise rotation of the knee. Repeat the exercise on the other leg.

Do not lean the body during this exercise. You will probably find that the standing leg has to work hard. This is because it is carrying all of your weight. After you have completed the exercise, give the legs a good shake to loosen them up again.

Exercise 8 – leg stretch

Stretching is an important part of the warm-up routine as it improves flexibility and helps the circulation of blood and stimulates the lymphatic system.

The three most important features of any stretching exercises are:

a The body should be warmed up. Under no circumstances should you try to perform any stretching routine without warming up first. For that reason, stretching exercises are included towards the end of this sequence.

b Take your time. If you are not quite as supple as you think you should be, there is a temptation to try and stretch too hard. This can be a huge setback if you damage yourself, as you will not be able to train for quite some time. As with any Tai Chi exercises, little and often is much better than trying to do everything at once.

c Breathe. This may seem trivial advice, but a very common mistake is to hold the breath during stretches. Keep the breathing deep and relaxed. This allows the blood to be rich in oxygen that nourishes the muscles and helps prevent damage.

Note: If a stretch causes pain, you are either trying to stretch too far or an injury is limiting the stretch. In either case the pain is a warning to stop or ease off.

1 Stand in the Wu Chi posture.

2 Slide the left leg straight back, and allow the right knee to bend. Rest both hands on the right knee. The intensity of the stretch is determined by how far back you move the left leg. For the best stretch, keep the toes of the left foot pointing as far forwards as possible.

3 Take a deep breath in. On the outward breath, push forward with the right knee. You will feel the stretch working along the back of the leg if you are performing it correctly. Do not allow the left heel to lift. It you cannot prevent this from happening, you are trying to stretch too far. Adjust, so that you have a shorter stance. On the inward breath, relax the stance so that the stretch relaxes. Let the knee move back and the body rise.

Repeat the stretch for ten breaths. When you have completed ten stretches with the left leg, change stance and do ten stretches with the right leg.

This sequence is repeated for both legs. A good number to start with is three batches of ten stretches for each leg. This should be varied according to your own fitness level.

Exercise 9 – adductor stretch

1 Start with your feet twice shoulder-width apart.
2 Sink down on to your right leg and try to hold your feet with your hands. If this is too much to start with hold your ankles instead. Keep both feet flat on

the floor. If you cannot keep your feet flat, your legs are too wide apart. Stretch the legs by gently bouncing with your breath for a count of ten.
3 If you cannot reach the floor, just go as low as is comfortable. Repeat on the other leg.

Exercise 10 – hurdler splits

1 Sit on the floor in the position shown.

2 Stretch your leg by lowering your torso to your leg.

3 If you cannot reach forward, just sitting in the position will stretch your legs.

Note: This is a powerful stretch and should not be attempted unless you are quite loose and warmed up.

Qi Exercises

The following exercises are intended for you to experiment with, rather than included as part of your daily routine. In the beginning, they may seem a little strange or even pointless. If you can repeat the exercises every now and then, you will start to understand their function. If you do decide to keep a logbook, the findings of these experiments will make interesting reading when you look back on your notes after a period of time (say a year).

The first exercise or "floppy arm", is probably the easiest to master. Try it with a friend, it can be fun if taken in that spirit. Remember, if you are happy, you will be more relaxed.

The next two exercises, "Unbreakable Arm" and "Energy Ball", are standard exercises for a martial arts or healing class. One of the major causes for not being able to gain results from the experiments is tension. If you find yourself becoming tense, the best advice is to try to make it more fun. Go back to the floppy arm experiment and try to laugh about it!

Floppy Arm

It is easy for tension to become "locked away" inside your body. One of the areas that becomes most affected by "locked in" tension is the shoulders. If your shoulders are tight, it can make the rest of your body stiff.

This experiment does not particularly try to give a long-term cure, but rather a diagnosis for tension in the shoulders.

1 Hold your partner's outstretched wrist.
2 Ask them to relax.

Now release the wrist.

1

2

What happened? There are two possible results from this:

1 The arm stayed where it was or dropped slightly.
2 The arm dropped to the person's side when you released it.

If the arm dropped to your partner's side the shoulders are fairly loose. If the arm stayed roughly where it was, there is tension or an unwillingness to "let go". Try the experiment again, but if your friend still cannot release the arm, do not worry. At least they know the first part of their Qigong training.

Unbreakable Arm

1 Start by standing opposite your partner and place your hand, palm upwards on their shoulder. Clench your fist as tight as you can and clench your arm muscles.
2 Your partner then tries to push down on your elbow and bend the joint. In this situation, you are using your muscular force to stop them. If you are stronger than them, you will be able to hold them back for some time. If they are stronger than you, it will be impossible to keep your arm straight. When you have experienced the feeling, relax – do not keep struggling!

3 Now place your open hand on your partner's shoulder. Keep it relaxed. Imagine that you are extending your intent through your fingertips to a great distance. Keep your muscles relaxed, but your intent strong.

4 Your partner is going to do the same again, but this time you will stop them with your intent. As your partner puts the pressure on, stay relaxed but keep your arm straight with intent. You will find that it is very difficult for them to bend your arm this time.

Energy Ball

1 Start by closing your eyes for a couple of minutes and breathing deeply for a few breaths. This is to get you tuned into the energy. If you are already quite sensitive, you may not need to do this.
2 Face the palms of your hands in towards each other. Keep your shoulders down and your arms relaxed. Gradually move your hands towards each other. At a certain point, you will pick up a sensation that feels like

an invisible force or heat in the gap between your hands. Play with the feeling, and see if you can make the "Energy Ball" between your hands bigger.
3 If you have a friend nearby who has been doing the same, face each other and make an "Energy Ball" between the middle of you. Try to feel its shape. Notice how the feeling changes if you or your friend moves away.

Makkaho Meridian Stretches

If you want to become supple, you need to stretch. As you stretch your muscles, it would be useful if you could work on specific energy meridians at the same time.

A common set of stretching exercises taught to Shiatsu students is the Makkaho set. These stretches work all of the classical meridians and the extended meridians that are used in Shiatsu, but are useful for anybody who is interested with keeping supple.

The stretches resemble Yoga stretches. The way to use them is similar. You should always stretch on the out breath and relax on the in breath. Do not bounce, as this can cause injury. Never attempt a deep stretch unless you are warmed up, and always know your own limits. Remember the most important rule for stretching – IF IT HURTS, STOP!

When you are coming out of the stretches, always come out the same way that you went in.

These stretches are based on the Taoist idea of the Five Elements. Each of the stretches emphasises a particular Element, i.e. Earth, Air, Fire, Water or Metal.

A - Metal stretch

This exercise stretches the lung and large intestine meridians. Viewed from the front, it resembles the letter "A".

Stand with your feet shoulder-width apart and link your thumbs behind your back. On an outward breath, bend your body forward. Work with the stretch for a few breaths before coming out of it.

Come out of the stretch on an outward breath. Do this by pushing your hands forwards and letting your body follow.

Change the grip on your thumbs and repeat the exercise.

The Metal stretch resembles the letter "A".

B - Earth stretch

This exercise stretches the stomach and spleen meridians. Viewed from the side, it resembles the letter "B".

1 Kneel on the floor.

2 Breathe out and lean back onto your elbows. (This may be as far as your body will stretch at the moment, if it feels like a big enough stretch, hold it for 2–3 breaths and come out of it.)

3 If you still have plenty of room left to stretch, breathe out and lower your back to the floor.

When coming out of the stretch, be sure to go through the stage where you place your elbows on the floor, otherwise you risk straining your back.

C - Fire stretch

This stretch works with the heart and small intestine meridians. It resembles the letter "C" when viewed from the side.

1 Sit with the soles of your feet together and draw them as close to your groin as you can. Grab your feet with your hands, keeping your elbows outside your shins.

2 On an outward breath, bend your body forward and release your neck.

56

D - Water stretch

This stretch will work the bladder and kidney meridians. From the side, it resembles the letter "D".

1 Sit with your legs out and your back straight.
2 On an exhalation, bend forwards and grab the start of the kidney meridian in the middle of the foot. If you cannot reach this point yet, just grab your ankles.
3 Increase the stretch by dropping your elbows and releasing your neck.

E - Secondary fire stretch

This stretch works the heart protector and triple heater meridians. From the side, it resembles the letter "E".

1 Sit with your legs crossed in front of you.
2 Cross your arms and touch your knees. If your left shin is in the front, your left forearm should be in front of the right. Exhale and lean forwards. Press on your knees to open your groin.
  Repeat, crossing your legs the other way.

F - Wood stretch

This stretch will work the gallbladder and liver meridians. When viewed from the front, it resembles the letter "F".

1 Sit with your legs fairly wide apart. Do not put your legs so wide that you cannot execute the stretch for your upper body.
Keep your back straight.
2 Exhale and lean to one side.

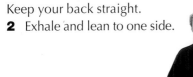

If you can reach, touch your big toe with the hand reaching over your head. With your other hand grab the next toe. If this is not yet possible, just grab the ankle. Do not collapse your abdomen.

Qi Self-massage

Exercises are not the only way to move your energy. A shiatsu or acupuncture therapist will use their skill to do exactly the same thing. If you were to take the simplest of their techniques and learn to apply them to yourself, you can start to learn how to be your own therapist. This could never take the place of having a fully trained therapist work on you, but it can be helpful in maintaining your health.

The following sequence contains useful techniques and can be practiced at any time of the day. It will take about 10 minutes once you have learned the sequence.

Massage the crown of your head

The crown point is where all the Yin meridians eventually meet up. Massage this point by rotating it gently with your fingertips. Bring intent from your fingertips down through your body.

Tap the head and neck

Keep your hands loose and tap your scalp and neck with the tips of your fingers.

Chi face wash

1 Rub your hands together until they are quite warm.

2 Rub your face and scalp with your warm hands as though you were washing it. When your hands cool off, warm them again by rubbing. Do not forget to wash behind your ears! There are many points around the ear.

Opening the forehead

Use your fingertips to smooth across your forehead.

Tap your shoulder

1 Make a loose fist with one hand and tap your shoulder and upper back.
2 It may help to use the other hand to push your elbow and help you reach further.

1

Opening the neck

Use the same movement to open the back of the neck.

Neck rotation

Keep your fingers at the base of your neck and gently rotate your neck from side to side.

2

Tap your arm

Tap along your inner arm moving outwards from your torso. Tap along the centre line and either side of it. This will stimulate the lung, pericardium and heart meridians.

Tap your outer arm from the fingertips to the shoulder. Tap along the centre line and either side of it. This will stimulate the large intestine, triple heater and small intestine meridians.

Tap your back

You will improve your range of movement if you bend forwards to tap your back. Pay attention to your sacrum (the area at the base of the spine) and try to tap along the bladder meridian.

Tap your legs

Tap down the outside to stimulate Yang meridians (bladder, stomach and gall bladder) and up the inside to stimulate Yin meridians (kidney, spleen and liver).

Tap your chest and abdomen

Use fingertips or loose fists to gently tap the chest and abdomen.

Massage your Hara

Spiral outwards from your navel in a clockwise direction.

Rotate your ankles and toes

1 Sit down and, using your hands, rotate your ankles.
2 Then rotate each of your toes.

Massage your knees

Massage behind the knee and gently move your kneecap to stimulate blood and Chi flow.

Massage your feet

Give a general massage to loosen your feet. Finish by massaging the start of the kidney meridian in the middle of your foot.

Flowing Qigong Sets

The following Qigong sets are examples of moving Qigong. All of the same rules apply that we have already covered. The most important of these are:

> **1** If it hurts, stop!
> **2** Do not try to do too much too fast. Gradually build up your practice time over a long period.
> **3** Do not force anything to happen. Your breathing and movements should be synchronised. Allow the exercises to work by breathing naturally – they will automatically synchronise after a little practice.
> **4** Stay relaxed.
> **5** Enjoy!

The flowing sets are very good for reducing tension because they relax the muscles and loosen the joints. Try to learn a full set of exercises if you can. If you like exercises from each set, there is no reason why you should not mix and match between the sets.

Qigong Set

SWING YOUR WAIST AND ARMS

This exercise has already been covered in the section for "Warm Ups" (see pages 40-51), but it is an excellent way to start this Qigong set.

1 Stand in the Wu Chi posture.
2 Oscillate to the left and then to the right. While you are moving the waist to the left and right, keep the body straight and the arms relaxed. Start quite slowly, but gradually build up speed. Do not become too vigorous with the movements, otherwise it will be difficult to keep the correct movements. You can, however, exert some effort into the exercise if you wish.

TAI CHI CIRCLE

This exercise teaches you how to breathe deeply and invigorate your body with a good supply of oxygen.

1 For this exercise all the breathing is done through your nose. Your position remains stationary. Try to let your mind empty and keep your body relaxed. Stand with your feet parallel and one shoulder-width apart. Look straight out in front of you with your eyes relaxed.

2 Turn your hands so that the palms face outwards.
3 On an inward breath, begin to raise both of your hands in a circular motion.
4 Keep your shoulders down and synchronise the movement with your breathing.
5 When your hands reach the top of the circle. Lower your shoulders, elbows and then press your palms down gently with the outward breath.

Start the movement again. When you become an expert at this exercise, you will be able to slow your breathing down so that it becomes deeper.

SHOULDER ROTATIONS

In order to relax your body and breathe deeper, you need to learn how to relax your shoulders. The next three exercises work on the shoulders.

1 Start by standing in the Wu Chi posture.
2 On an inward breath, lift the shoulders. Time the lifting of the shoulders to synchronise with the inward breath. When the lungs are full and the shoulders are at their maximum, slowly let the breath out and allow the shoulders to descend.

Repeat the movement several times, and then change the direction of the shoulder rotation. Try to do the movement quite slowly, so that it is easier to time the rise and fall of the shoulders with the movement of the breath.

SHOULDER ROTATION WITH EXTENDED ARMS

This exercise is a more difficult version of the previous one. Attempt it only when you feel confident with the previous exercise.

1 Start by standing in the Wu Chi posture.
2 On an inward breath, imagine that your intake of air fills your arms and let them float upwards.
3 Stop when they are slightly lower than your shoulders.

4 Rotate your shoulders several times in both directions (the same way that you did for the last exercise). You will find that the exercise is made more difficult because your hands are raised.

5 Try and keep them in the same position, but do not lock your shoulder joints.

It normally takes many years of practice before you can perform this exercise without moving your shoulders at all.

WINDMILLS

This exercise takes on different dimensions depending on whether you practice it fast or slow.

1 Start by standing in the Wu Chi posture.
2 Throw your hand backwards over your shoulder and begin to rotate one of your arms. Reverse the direction of rotation.
3 Repeat step 2 with the other arm.
4 An interesting variation is to swing both arms at the same time. Try both in the same direction at first and then in opposite directions.

SPINE TWIST WITH ARMS EXTENDED

This exercise is useful for unlocking your spine and keeps it healthy and supple. Avoid risk of injury by taking the exercise very slowly.

1 Start by standing in the Wu Chi posture.
2 On the start of an inward breath, bend your wrists slightly as shown.
3 Do not pull your wrist too far back as this will cause tension and restrict energy flow. Continue the inward breath and allow your arms to float to shoulder level.

4 When you release the air from your lungs slowly, rotate the upper part of your body. Co-ordinate the rotation with your outward breath.
5 When you breathe in again, bring your body back to the central position.
6 Repeat the exercise by twisting your body in the other direction.

Five or six repetitions will be enough at first. You may increase the amount as you become more supple.

WAIST ROTATIONS

If you can keep your waist supple, you will have kept the centre of your movement free. This will help your agility and co-ordination.

1 Start by standing in the Wu Chi posture.
2 Place the centre of your hands on your kidney area. Push your pelvis forwards and keep looking straight ahead. If you fix your focus on a stationary object, it will help you to keep your head steady.

3 Rotate your waist in either direction. Try and move your mid-section in a circle, so that you work evenly through your body. Breathe deeply with the movements.

When you have repeated several rotations, reduce the size of the circles of rotation and come to the centre. Do not suddenly stop in mid-flight.
Repeat steps 2 and 3, with your waist rotating in the other direction.

SIDE PUSH IN HORSERIDING STANCE

This balances the left and right sides of your body, primarily the gallbladder meridian.

1 Stand with your feet parallel and approximately twice shoulder width apart. Do not try to do the exercise with your feet too far apart, as this will cause you to poke the base of your spine out when you sink in the next part of the exercise. This stance is called the horseriding stance and is common to many martial arts exercises and techniques.

2 Start your inward breath and raise your arms to shoulder height.

3 Continue the inward breath and drop your elbows. As they drop, sink your torso. It is important to keep your back straight. If you find this difficult, start again in a narrower horseriding stance.

4 Try and time your in breath, so that it reaches capacity when you have dropped to your lowest position.

5 On the outward breath, push down with your feet and out with your hands. This will lift your torso and extend your arms. If you keep the upper half of your body relaxed, your hands will move in a roughly circular pattern.

Repeat steps 2 to 5 several times.

SIDE STRETCH IN HORSERIDING STANCE

This stretch helps to keep the energy meridians in the side of the body healthy.

1 Start in the horseriding stance that was used in the previous exercise.
2 Lift your arms to shoulder level and have the palms of your hands facing outwards. This is the neutral position for the exercise.
3 Breathe in and make an "S" shape with your arms.
4 Stretch on the outward breath. Do the stretch by pushing your hands in opposite directions.

Keep your arm over your ear and do not lean in the forward or backward planes. If you feel unstable on your feet, start again but use a narrower horseriding stance.

Repeat the exercise three times.

Come back to the "neutral position", explained in step 2. Make the "S" shape with your arms, but this time, the opposite way to that in step 3. Repeat the stretches on the other side of your body. Come back to the neutral position and, either start the stretching sequence again, or finish the exercise.

FORWARD AND BACKWARD BENDS

This will keep your spine supple and strong and therefore less prone to injury. It will also invigorate energy in your bladder meridian.

1 Start in the Wu Chi posture.
2 Breathe in and lift your hands to shoulder level.

3 Breathe out and lower your hands. This is the same as the opening movement of the Tai Chi form.
4 Breathe in, raise your arms and lean back. Keep your chin tucked in and look forwards. Your arms are in a circular shape as if you were holding a large beach ball. Do not lean back too far.

5 On the outward breath drop your body into a forward bend. This should be quite relaxed. You do not need to try and stretch in this position, just let your spine release itself.

6 Bend your knees, so that you are in a squatting position. The work here is done with your legs. Avoid back strain by keeping your back relaxed and in the same position. Let your legs take the effort.

7 Stand up by straightening your legs. Do not bend your back. If your arms are relaxed, your hands will naturally come together at the Tan Tien point on your abdomen.

Either repeat steps 1 to 7 or finish.

11. HIP ROTATION

Hip problems are common in old age. If you invest some time in this exercise it may save you problems with your hip joints in later life. You should practise these exercises with both legs.

1 Lift the knee of your leg as high as you can.

2 Rotate the knee three times in a clockwise direction.

3 Keep rotating, but stop if it begins to hurt.

4 Rest for a while by placing your foot on the floor.

Lift your knee again and rotate it in the opposite direction (anticlockwise). Rest your leg again.

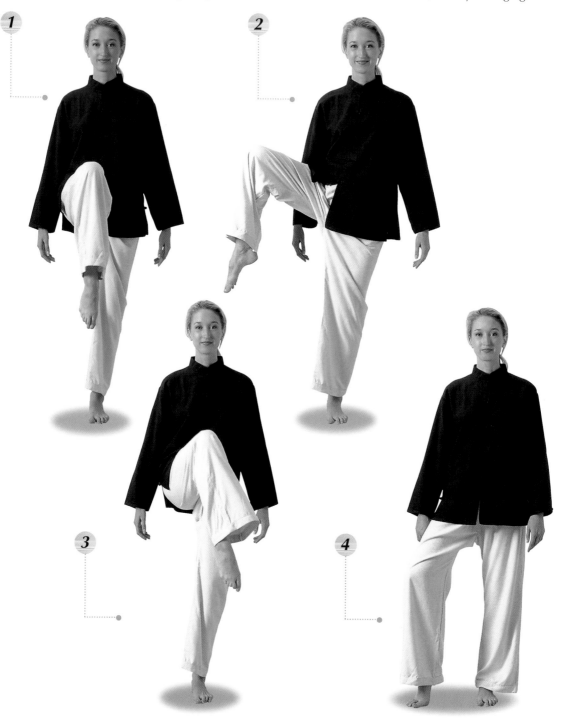

5 Lift your knee again.
6 Push your heel in a forward circle, as though you were thrusting your foot out.
7 Rest your leg again.

Reverse the direction of the last turn, so that the motion is similar to stamping on the floor.

The easy way to remember the exercise is that you will rotate your knee in the forward, backward, clockwise and anticlockwise directions.

If you find it difficult to balance, keep your eyes fixed on a mark on the wall and try to keep the marker steady. This will help you to keep the upper half of your body steady.

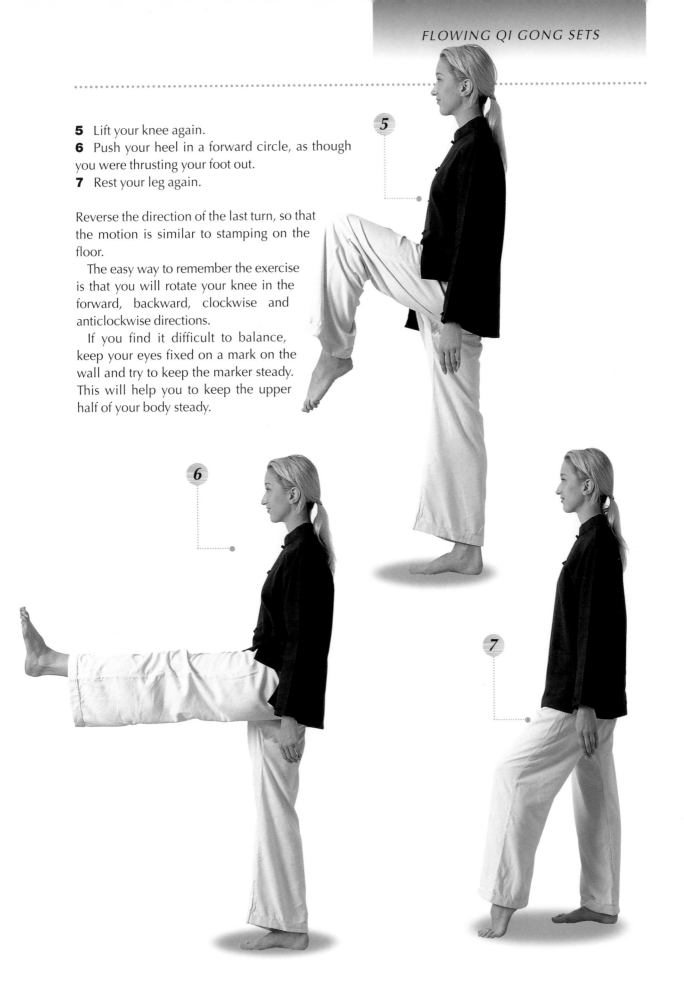

HEEL LIFTS

This exercise will tone the back of your legs and strengthen your ankles.

1 Stand in the Wu Chi postures. Press your palms to the floor and point your fingers inwards slightly.
2 On your inward breath, press down with your hands and lift your heels. Your fingers rotate to point forwards. On the outward breath, lower your heels to half way down and bring your hands back to the position that they were in for step 1.

On the next inward breath, lift your heels and rotate your hands, the same as in step 2. Breath out and gently lower your heels, so that you are back in your original starting position 1.

Repeat several times.

If you want to increase the difficulty of the exercise, then hold yourself in the high position 2 for a couple of breaths. You will find that this will test your balance and improve the strength in your legs.

The final exercises in this sequence are fairly demanding and should only be attempted with care after thoroughly warming up.

SWIMMING DRAGON

This exercise is good for stretching your legs and working your lungs. Work both sides equally.

1 Stand in the Wu Chi posture.
2 Slide your right foot forwards as far as is comfortable. Your left leg should be straight but not locked and your right knee is bent. This is the same as a long version of the bow stance (see page 34).

3 On the inward breath, push down with your right foot to raise your body and lift your arms above your head. Keep your breathing rhythmic and your body relaxed. Do not lift your shoulders with your arms.
4 On the outward breath, bend your right leg and let your arms drop.
5 This should be controlled. Do not just drop to the low stance.

Repeat the movements (3) and (4) several times. Perform the same exercise with your left leg forward, the same number of times.

CANDLESTICK

The shape of your body posture in this exercise should be straight like a candlestick. Be careful to not lean your torso to the side.

1 Stand with your legs approximately twice shoulder-width apart.

2 Raise your hands in front of your face.
3 Open your arms, so that your palms face outwards.
4 On an outward breath, shift all of your weight onto your right leg and drop your body down on to it. This will stretch your left leg.

5 Breath in and come back to the centre. Keep your arms stationary. This time you will be in a more crouched position than for step 4.

6 Shift all of your weight on to your left leg, the same way that you have just done for your right leg. Remember, do not lean in any direction.

7 Come back to the centre again, in the lower position.

Repeat the sequence several times.

WINE GLASS

Imagine that you have a full wine glass on the palm of your hand. Try to complete the exercise in a way that you will not "spill the wine".

1 Start in the Wu Chi posture. Push your right leg forward so that you are in the bow stance (see p34). Raise your right hand and imagine that you have a glass of wine balancing on it.
2 Shift your weight onto your left leg, and point your fingers inwards. Continue the path with your right hand as you sink down slightly further.
3 Shift your weight forward onto your right leg.

4 Shift your weight again onto your left leg and arch your back slightly. Look up to your hand, which should be above your face.
5 Push your weight back onto your right leg and allow your hand to come back to the original position. Try to make the movement smooth and continuous.

Repeat the steps several times. Perform the exercise again on the left side of your body, the same number of times. If you are feeling adventurous, try the exercise with both hands moving and your feet in the Wu Chi posture.

THE FROG

This exercise requires a good sense of balance. It stimulates the kidney meridian.

1 Stand with your feet slightly wider than shoulder-width apart.

2 Turn your toes outwards.

3 Bend your knees slightly, to lower your weight.

4 Hold your hands and arms as though you are holding a large ball in front of your chest. Alternate the position of your hands with your breath as you breathe deeply and slowly.

Qigong and Tai Chi

The training of Tai Chi and Qigong are very close in many aspects. The fact that they have shared geographical origins no doubt contributes to their similarity. In fact, Qigong and Tai Chi can be regarded as different aspects of the same study.

This fact has been used by Taoist Masters throughout the ages. When practising Tai Chi forms, one should be as sensitive to energy as a Qigong practitioner. When practising Qigong, your intent should be as keen as that of a martial artist.

A common method of practice is to take small parts of the Tai Chi form, and use them as Qigong exercises. This has the advantage of simplifying the movement. One can learn the basics of Tai Chi without having to learn a long and complicated sequence of movements. This allows the Qigong student to exploit the knowledge of Tai Chi and the Tai Chi student to perfect their moves.

The following exercises are taken from the Yang style of Tai Chi. For each exercise, there are two levels of practice. The first level is to teach you the basic movement and is practised in the Wu Chi posture.

When you have mastered the movement in the Wu Chi posture, the next level is to learn how to execute the movement in the posture in which it is practised in the Tai Chi form. This will encourage you to learn how to transfer your weight between legs and improve the co-ordination of your upper and lower body.

RAISE THE HANDS (OPENING FORM)

This deceptively simple move is the opening movement for many Tai Chi patterns.

Easy level

1 Stand in the Wu Chi posture.

2 Extend your fingertips. Point your fingertips forwards.

3 On an inhalation, push your fingertips outwards and simultaneously raise your hands.

4 On the exhalation, press your hands down. Repeat the cycle.

Harder level
At the final part of the exhalation, relax your groin and bend your knees slightly. When you inhale, lift your body with the movement. This will work your legs harder as you sink into the posture.

TWO-HANDED PUSH

Keep your elbows relaxed and do not lock your elbow joints on the push.

Easy level

1 Stand in the Wu Chi posture.

2 Extend your hands in front of your body.

3 On an inhalation, draw your hands inwards by sinking your elbows.

4 On the exhalation, push with both hands.

Harder level

1 This movement should be executed in the bow stance. Sink your weight back on to the rear leg as you inhale.

2 When you exhale and push, transfer your weight to the leading leg.

STRUM THE LUTE

This circular movement is said to resemble the action of playing a musical instrument.

Easy level

1 Stand in the Wu Chi posture.

2 Extent your right hand in front of you.

3 Simultaneously, turn your waist to pull your left hand back and raise your left fingertips.

4 Keep the movement active with your waist and your hands, to complete the circle.

Harder level

Practise the movement in the empty stance and your weight on your right leg. This will improve your balance and strengthen the leg. You may wish to equalise the exercise by practising with the left leg as your standing leg.

BRUSH AND PUSH

In the Tai Chi sequence, brush and push is a block followed by a strike.

Easy level

1 Stand in the Wu Chi posture.

2 Position your left hand forward and your right hand back.

3 Press your left hand down as your right hand raises.

4 Twist your waist back to the centre and press out with your right hand and down with your left.

Repeat steps 2 to 4 with right and left hands reversed. The movement becomes cyclical when you start again at step 2.

Harder level

Practise the movement in the bow stance (see p34). Try with both a right and left legged bow stance. Your weight should move forward as you push outwards.

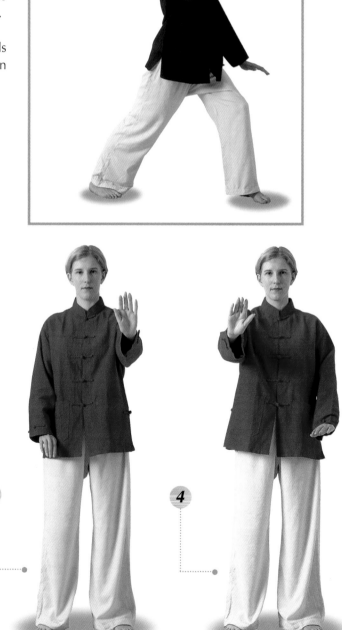

1

2

3

4

REPULSE MONKEY

In Taoist symbolism, the monkey represents the "chatter" that our minds seem to like so much. This exercise can help you to quieten that chatter for a more meditative state of mind.

Easy level

1 Stand in the Wu Chi posture.

2 Inhale, turn your waist to the right and begin to open your arms.

3 Turn and open your arms until you reach this position.

4 On the exhalation, push with your right hand and pull back with your left elbow.

Inhale, turn your waist to the left and open your arms. On the exhalation, push with your left hand and pull back with your right elbow.

Repeat the sequence.

Harder level
Try to do the exercise in the empty stance. If you
become proficient at that, try stepping backwards
as you perform the exercise.

PARTING THE WILD HORSE'S MANE

This exercise will emphasise any co-ordination faults with the upper and lower body.

Easy level

1 Stand in the Wu Chi posture.

2 Inhale, turn your waist to the right and position your left forearm below your right forearm.

3 Exhale and turn your waist to the centre. Extend your left hand forward and press down with your right.

Inhale, turn your waist to the left and position your right forearm below your left forearm.

Repeat the sequence.

Harder level

Try this movement as you step forward in the bow stance (see p34).

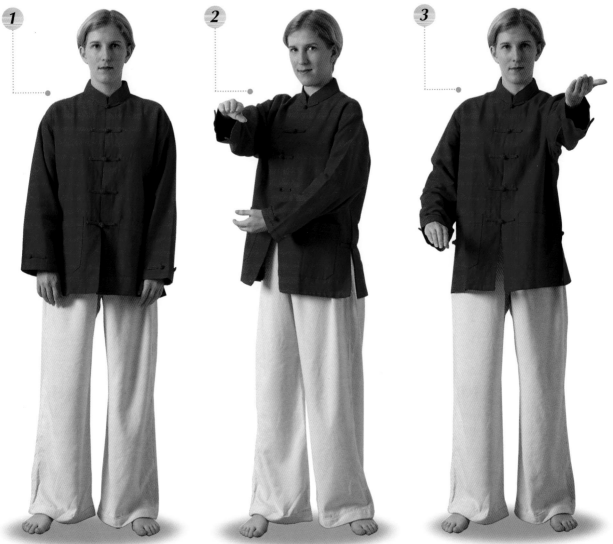

NEEDLE AT THE SEA BOTTOM

This exercise will strengthen your legs and back, especially when you try the harder level.

Easy level

1 Stand in the Wu Chi posture.

2 Push the fingertips of your right hand forward as you exhale.

3 On the inhalation, turn your waist to the right and relax your right elbow.

4 Push the fingertips out again, as in step 2.

Harder level

Start by trying the exercise with the other hand.

When you have mastered both hands, try the exercise in the empty stance. When you push your fingertips forward, sink your weight to a low position. Keep your back straight. Do not try and sink so low that your back arches.

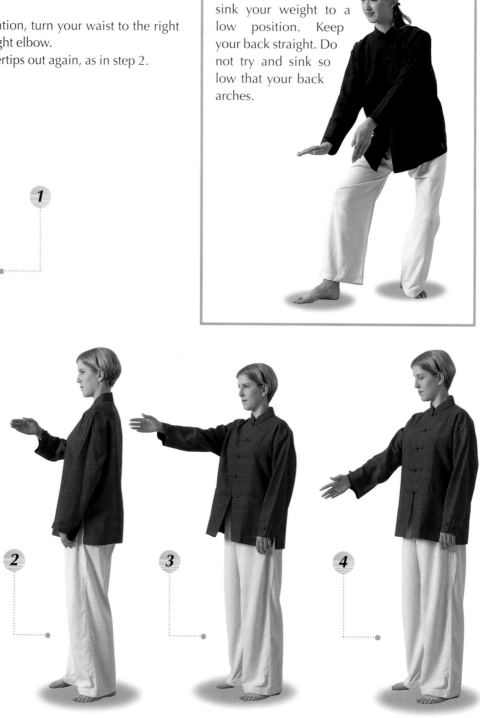

1

2

3

4

WAVING HANDS LIKE CLOUDS

This exercise works primarily with the arms, but do not make the common mistake of forgetting the legs!

Easy level

1 Stand in the Wu Chi posture.

2 Place your right hand in front of your throat and your left hand in front of your groin.

3 Exhale and turn your body to the right. Press down with your right hand and up with your left. Do not over reach.

4 Inhale and come back to the centre, this time with your hands reversed (i.e. left hand in the high position).

5 Exhale and turn your body to the left. Press down with your left hand and up with your right.

Repeat the sequence.

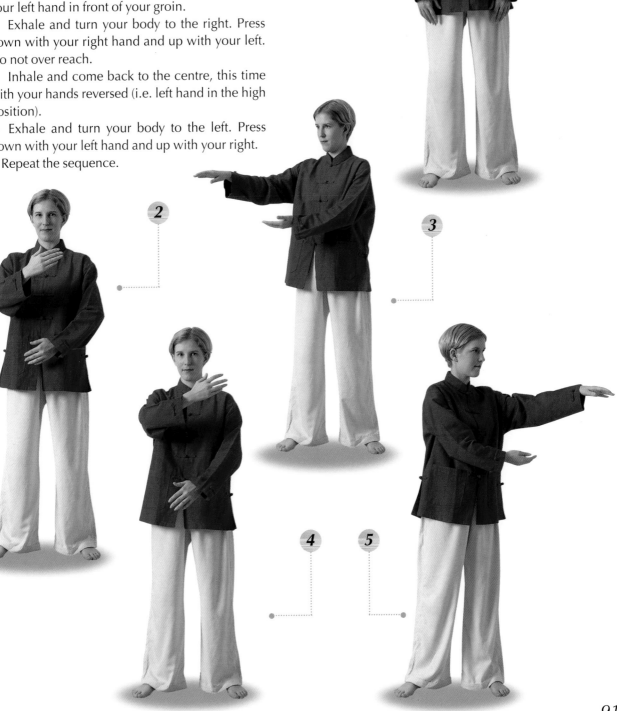

Harder level

Try the exercise with a wider stance. In some styles, wide stances are used for this exercise, to enhance your suppleness. Remember that it is better to have a narrow stance if you have a tendency to lean to one side.

Static Tai Chi postures

In the Tai Chi sequence, the martial artist will execute a number of postures that are joined seamlessly together to create continuous movement. Any of these postures can be used as a standing Qi gong exercise. Indeed, it is also true that this type of training is used in other traditional martial arts such as Tae Kwon Do and Karate.

The advantage of this type of training is that it helps you to build up stamina and resilience in the same way as the "Standing like a Tree" exercises, but is directly applied to the martial art that you may be studying.

The following four postures are taken from the Yang style of Tai Chi. Do not feel limited to these postures. If you are studying another style, pick a movement that frequently appears and practice standing in the posture for a few minutes every day. You may not notice the difference immediately, but your instructor will!

Single Whip

This is a useful posture because it is very expansive. Practising moves such as this for a period of time will help you to develop power within your movements.

Raise Hands

This movement would be a good one to follow Single Whip. The reason for this is that the energy is contracting rather than expanding. Practising both will help you to feel the difference. Be careful that you do not lean forwards.

White Crane Spreads its Wings

This movement plays with opposites. You need to keep your right arm raised, but your shoulder down. As with all standing postures, you should keep your intent strong but your body relaxed. This is easier said than done when you have all of your weight balancing on one leg!

Double Push

The double push is used frequently throughout most Tai Chi forms. As a push has the same body dynamics as a punch, the posture is almost universal throughout the martial arts. Remember, you do not need to look at your hands - they will not fall off!

Ba Duan Jin Exercises

The following sequence of Qigong exercises is called Ba Duan Jin. The name "Ba Duan Jin", roughly translates as "Eight Pieces of Silk". My interpretation of the name is that the exercises teach you to be soft and strong like silk.

The actual exercises date back to the beginnings of Qigong and have been used in various forms ever since they were devised. Different schools have placed a different emphasis on various ways of executing the moves. Drawings that are recognisable as this sequence have been found dating back to the 200 BC.

There are eight of these exercises. For convenience, and an easy number to remember, try starting with eight repetitions of each of the exercises. Don't worry if you lose count of how many you have done, it will not matter.

SUPPORTING THE SKY

This exercise will stretch all of your meridians and invigorate their energy, it is therefore relieving for fatigue.

1 Stand in the Wu Chi posture.
2 Raise your hands to forehead level.
3 Exhale and press upwards with your hands.
4 When your arms are extended, raise your heels slightly.
5 Inhale and bring your hands back to the level of your forehead.

  Repeat.

DRAWING THE BOW

This exercise is good for detoxifying your lungs.

1 Stand in the Wu Chi posture.

2 Inhale and raise your hands to a central position. One hand is closed and the other is open.

3 On the exhalation, press out with your left hand and pull back with your right, in the same motion as shooting a bow.

4 Relax to a central position on the inhalation.

Repeat the movement on the other side for the next exhalation.

CROSS STRETCH

This movement is beneficial to the spleen and stomach.

1 Stand in the Wu Chi posture.
2 Prepare to push simultaneously up and down with your hands.

3 On an exhalation, push upwards with one hand and downwards with the other.

Repeat on the other side. Exercise both sides evenly.

GAZING BACK AT THE MOON

This exercise works with the meridians that govern the central nervous system. It is also helpful for correcting bad postural habits. This exercise is not suitable for pregnant women.

1 Stand in the Wu Chi posture.

2 Raise your arms in front of your chest.

3 Turn the whole of your upper body as you exhale and push outwards with your hands. Keep your arms straight, do not let them wander to either side.

4 Come back to the central position on an inhalation.

Repeat the exercise on the other side.

SIDE STRETCH

This exercise will work with the easily neglected meridians on the side of your body. It is not suitable for pregnant women.

1 Stand in the Wu Chi posture.

2 Raise your right hand over your head.

3 Exhale and bend over to the side. Stay relaxed, being careful not to over-stretch. On the last part of your exhalation, lift the heel of your inside leg, to increase the stretch

Return to the centre. Repeat on the other side.

KNEE BEND

This exercise demands high strength in your legs. Do not dip too low, until you know that you are capable of doing it without sustaining injury. This exercise is not suitable for pregnant women.

1 Stand in the Wu Chi posture.
2 Extend your arms to the sides. Inhale.
3 Exhale and press down with your hands as you bend your knees.
4 Straighten up as you inhale. Move your arms ready to press down with another exhalation.
  Press down again on the exhalation.

CLENCHING THE FISTS

This is not a punching exercise. It should be done slowly and is designed to increase the flow of your Chi. This exercise is not suitable for pregnant women.

1 Stand in the Wu Chi posture.
2 Bend your knees slightly to drop your weight.

3 Clench your fists at the side of your body. Note that the thumb is held inside the fist, which would make it impractical for punching.
4 On the exhalation, drive your fist forward in a twisting motion.
5 Inhale and bring the fist back to the centre.
6 Repeat on the other side.

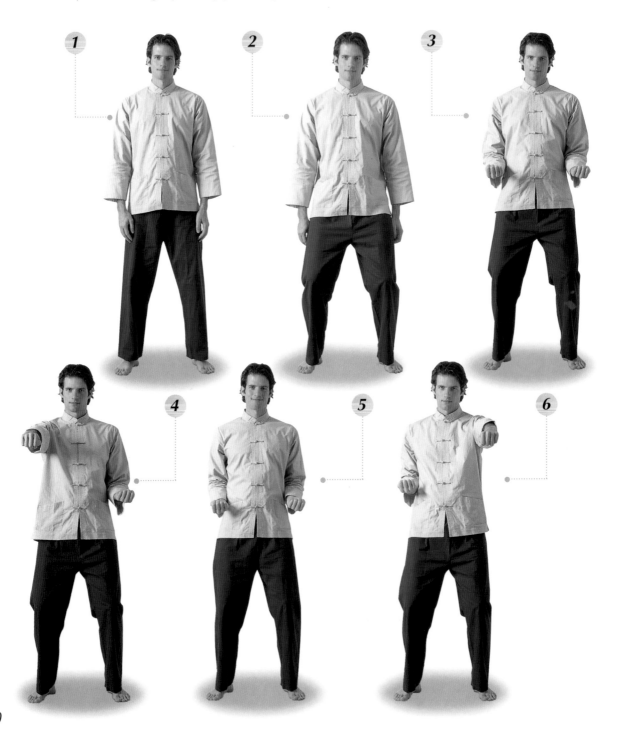

SHAKING

This exercise is said to stimulate the lymphatic system and therefore aid the immune system. It is not suitable for pregnant women.

1 Stand in the Wu Chi posture.
2 Place the backs of your hands on to your kidney area.
3 Inhale deeply. Make your exhalation long and shake your body for the duration.
  Repeat.

Static Qigong Sets

Static or standing Qigong has been the core of many Qigong and martial arts' styles for many years. The sequence shown here is one of the more popular routines called "Standing Like a Tree". Use the idea of the tree, it has deep roots and is difficult to topple.

When you first start the exercise, it will probably feel quite difficult. This is because you have never done anything like it before. Build up your practice in small stages and you will develop great internal strength and stamina.

Position 1 – Wu Chi

We already know and understand the Wu Chi posture from our other exercises. It is a good idea to relax your body and mind at the beginning of a standing session with a couple of minutes standing in the Wu Chi posture.

Position 2 – Holding a balloon

When you can stand in Wu Chi for five minutes comfortably, you can move to the next exercise. This exercise starts in the Wu Chi posture but is more advanced.

1 Start in the Wu Chi posture.
2 Bend your knees slightly but keep your back straight. It should feel as if you were sitting on the edge of a chair but keeping the weight in your legs. You will feel your thigh muscles being worked. If you are not sure about your back alignment, stand against a wall at first so that you can build an internal reference.
3 Raise your arms into the position shown. Imagine that you are holding a three-dimensional balloon in you arms. Do not squash it against your chest.

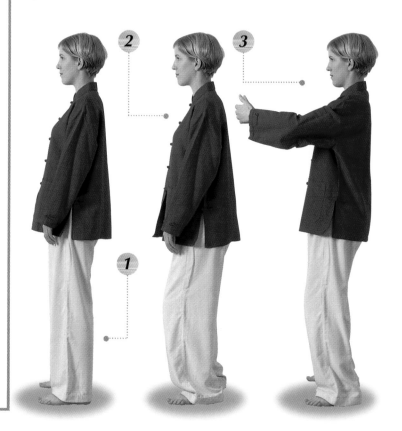

Position 3 – Holding your belly

This exercise allows you to rest those aching shoulders!

1 Start from the second position, still holding the balloon.
2 Drop your arms to the lower position shown. Be aware of any internal changes that happen during or after this transition.

Position 4 - Standing in a stream

This exercise will improve your sense of grounding or rooting.

Turn your hands outwards and press down as shown. Imagine that you are standing in a stream of running water and that you need to sink your weigh to stop it from washing you away. Imagine that your arms are resisting against their natural buoyancy in the water.

Position 5 - Raising your arms

This is the most demanding of all the standing positions because your arms are in an elevated position. Try and stay relaxed and do not practise it for too long until you are accustomed to it.

1 Start in the second position, holding the balloon.
2 Raise and rotate your arms to the position shown.

The Full Cycle

The next step, once you have learned to stand in all the positions, is to do them one after the other. This is an advanced way of practising, but will cause no harm as long as you do not try to do too much too quickly.

The sequence is useful, but not vital. As long as you start and finish with the Wu Chi posture, you can practise as many or as few of the exercises as you choose. If you want to try the sequence, but find it too demanding, try standing in the Wu Chi posture between stances.

Qi gong Meditation

One of the interesting (and sometimes amusing) aspects of studying ancient systems such as Taoism is the "new discoveries" that are made connected to them. Modern science is constantly finding new ways of expressing old ideas.

Meditation is one such discipline that has come under scrutiny in recent times. It has always been said by participants that meditation helps them to de-stress and heal themselves. Modern scientists and psychologists are now measuring the effect of meditation with such devices as magnetic resonance imaging and agreeing that meditation can have very beneficial effects.

One of the first things that many find when they start mediation is that once they start to relax, they fall asleep. The meaning of this is usually quite simple – you are tired. The first meditation exercise, "Onion Skin", is useful should you find this happening. The idea is that you peel off "layers" of tension, like an onion skin, with your intent.

It is quite normal to actually fall asleep during this meditation, but if you do, your body will hopefully be more relaxed, and your sleep more restful.

The second meditation "Inner Smile", should be practiced whenever possible! In it we learn how to harness the power of a smile and turn it inwards to ourselves for healing.

"Onion Skin"

a Lie down on the floor, placing support under your head if it makes you more comfortable. Do not use a large pillow as this will push your neck forward.

b Close your eyes and relax. Keep your mouth gently closed. Breathe through the nose. Focus your mind on your breathing letting it become soft and deep. Spend a few minutes focusing the attention on your breathing, allowing it to become soft and regular.

c Bring your attention to your forehead. Relax the muscles and skin on your forehead. Do this by imagining that every time you breathe out, the

tension is just falling away. Do the same for your eyes and the muscles of your face.

d Work down through the body relaxing your neck, shoulders, arms, chest, abdomen, waist, thighs, knees, lower legs, ankles and feet.

e When your attention reaches your feet, pause for a while by bringing your attention back to your breathing. Make sure that your breathing is still relaxed, deep and regular.

f Repeat by bringing your intention through your body again, starting at your forehead. Imagine that each time you re-start your sweep through your body, you are removing a "layer" of tension. These "layers" are like the layers of the onion skin. If you can reach seven or eight layers before falling asleep, you will achieve a high level of relaxation. If you do fall asleep, sweet dreams!

"Inner Smile"

Look at the two pictures below:

Do you feel a difference when you look at the pictures? Does the happy face give you a tiny lift?

This is the power of the smile, and you were only looking at a picture. Notice how happiness and laughter tend to be contagious. The energy of the smile is spreading between different people when this happens. As we all know, being happy makes you feel good.

Now remember a happy or funny event that has happened to you. If it makes you laugh a little, even better. Keep the image and feel the warmth of the smile deep within you. Imagine that the warmth or light from the smile is spreading through your organs and then through the rest of your body. Let the inner happiness spread throughout your body and chase out any negative feelings.

This simple meditation can even be done while reading how to do it (I even felt good writing it!). Imagine the effect of the smile spreading and use your sensitivity to notice the changes it creates.

This meditation is powerful to use as a sitting meditation. It is a good starter meditation as it requires no belief in any systems or theories, just the ability to imagine a smile spreading through your body.

Try the meditation in a sitting position with your eyes closed. Relax your breathing and let the smile take over.

Qigong in Daily Life

You have reached the end of the book. That fact alone probably means that you are interested with how Qigong can be used to improve your life. You now know that correct use of posture and breathing is beneficial to your health and wellbeing. The concept of energy is not alien to you and you understand the idea that good energy flow promotes good health.

"If Qigong is so good then, why doesn't everybody do it?" is a reasonable question to ask at this point. One of the most important reasons for this is the time that the training takes. Some of the traditional oriental texts talk about training for years before getting any benefits. If it is going to take that long, most people will not bother in the first place.

There is a way around the problem. If you use Qigong as a reference point in your life, then you can revise the way that you do things in a way that much of your life becomes similar to training. For example, some of the most common problems with modern people arise from sitting at a desk or steering wheel for long periods.

If you think about what you've learned in Qigong, when you are at your desk, you may find yourself sitting in a more healthy posture. This means that you will be healthier and that your Qigong practice is constantly rectifying the damage that you did to yourself by sitting in the wrong position.

The main things to watch out for when checking your sitting position in this way are keeping your head up and shoulders down. Sit in front of your work, not at an angle and keep your breathing as relaxed as you can. Suddenly your sitting position is the same as the one that you use for sitting meditation. This will train your body to be able to sit for longer periods comfortably when practising your meditation.

One final word about posture, holding the telephone between your shoulder and ear is a major cause of neck and shoulder problems. How can your head be up and your shoulder relaxed in such a position?

You do not have to learn advanced skills such as healing to benefit from Qigong.

Conclusion

Qigong is a multi-faceted art that involves training your mind, body and spirit. Through fairly simple exercises and meditations, the user can learn how to integrate body and mind more fully, so that both can be kept in better health.

There are many different versions of Qigong. The training will tend to vary depending on the results that are sought. For example, a Shaolin monk will practise in a different way to the office professional who wants to learn how to maintain their health efficiently.

The subject of Qigong is deep. It involves learning about different aspects of the body and mind that would not be approached by many people were it not for Qigong. The hope is that by learning to understand one's own needs in a better and less egotistical way, then one can understand and respect other people's needs.

There are many good teachers about. There are no hard and fast rules about how to determine who is a good teacher and who is just trying to make a little extra money. It is hoped that this book will enable the reader to make a better-informed decision before investing time and money in a teacher.

For me, the quick test is how a teacher responds to a question. If you are given a straightforward answer, then that teacher can teach you what you need to know at that moment. If a teacher demands that you accept a fact without some kind of proof, or verification, take it as a warning sign.

The world of Qigong is as varied as it is fascinating. All that remains is to wish all readers good health and hope that you enjoy your discovery of Qigong.

Index

Credits and Acknowledgements

First and foremost I would like to thank my wife, Carol and my parents for their love and support throughout this and many other projects.

My teachers and influences are too numerous to mention here. I would like to thank the following for the enduring patience they showed whilst teaching me different parts of the subject; Sue Hix and Tom Litten of the Rosewell Shiatsu Centre (for my Shiatsu training), Chris Pei and Shelagh Grandpierre of the Tai Chi Alliance (for my Tai Chi training), Kris Larthe of the Healing Tao Centre in London (for meditation training), Chun Chen of Universe Tai Chi (for many of the movements) and Nick Scarr for teaching me the Ba Duan Jin and many other fun things.

The author and publishers would also like to thank the models: Martin Arno, Caron Bosler and Karita Lightfoot.

Additional images:
11bl, 13 br, 14 cl, 14tr, 15tr, 26bl, 27, 28tl, 28bl, 106, 109bl {c} Stockbyte. (where b = bottom, c = centre, l = left, r = right, t = top)
Illustrations pp18-19 by Pauline Cherrett